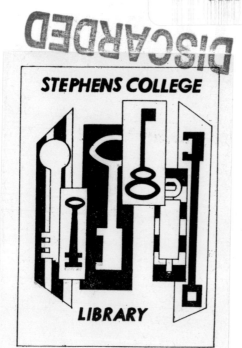

Tales of the Hodja

Tales of the Hodja

RETOLD BY

Charles Downing

ILLUSTRATED BY

WILLIAM PAPAS

NEW YORK

HENRY Z. WALCK, INC.

1965

PRINTED IN AUSTRIA BY DRUCKEREI ERWIN METTEN
CANISIUSGASSE 8-10 WIEN IX

DEDICATED TO
Matthieu Renieris
*who first introduced
the Compiler to the Hodja*

INTRODUCING
THE HODJA...

NASREDDIN Hodja is one of the most celebrated personalities of the Middle East, the Balkans and Greece. He is much more alive there than Sinbad the Sailor or Aladdin, for his words and deeds arise from the everyday life of the people and make them laugh in what is sometimes a very earnest world. *Nasreddin*, which should strictly be written *Nasr-ed-Dīn*, is his given name, the Muslim equivalent of a Christian name, and means 'Helper of the Faith'. Until 1935, when such terms of address were abolished in Turkey, *Hodja* was an honorary title denoting a scholar, in particular one learned in the Qoran and religious law. It bestowed upon its bearer the privilege of wearing the special head-dress called in Turkish the *kavuk*, a felt cap enveloped by a white cloth or *saryk*. That this may sometimes have been worn on a head that thus had more outward than inward signs of learning is hinted at in the story where the Hodja, having failed to read a badly written letter, says to his enquirer, who upbraids him for wearing the *kavuk* under false pretences: 'You put it on, and see if *you* can read the letter!' (p. 25). Persian culture exerted a great influence over that

of the Turks, and a *hodja* would be expected to be able to read Persian; some tales, however, not retold here for reasons of language, show that the Hodja's Persian was no better than many an English scholar's French. The title of *hodja* enabled Nasreddin to perform many functions in society. Islam is a religion which has no professional priesthood, and a learned man, who knew the Arabic of the Qoran, might act as *khātib* or preacher in the mosque, or as *imām* or prayer-leader. He might also perform the civil functions of *cadi* or magistrate, or be appointed a schoolmaster. Or, as often happened to the Hodja, he might be out of work and pass his time in the coffee-house, or ploughing his plot of land, or selling salted vegetables, or, when times were bad, scrumping apples from a neighbour's orchard. But however low he might fall, the *hodja* still had a venerable rank in a society which, perhaps because it was its rarest commodity, valued learning. When the Hodja protests that he has no clothes befitting his position in which to appear before the *cadi*, the infidel merchant, the plaintiff in the case, fully understands, and provides him with some (p. 38). However, the Hodja is rarely helpless. When really pressed, he can earn pomegranates from keen seekers after knowledge (p. 36), or invent the office of 'shadow-*cadi*' (p. 23).

It is difficult to decide whether the Hodja was ever in fact a real person. The Turks treat Nasreddin Hodja as a historical personage

and display his *türbe* or mausoleum in Ak-Shehir ('White City') near Konya in Asiatic Turkey, where he is supposed to have settled, but the date of 386 of the Muslim era, equivalent to A.D. 993, inscribed there as his date of birth is certainly false. Many of the tales in his name cite Sivri-Hisar, the name of which, meaning 'Hill-top Castle', refers to the ruins of a Byzantine fortress overlooking the town as his place of birth; others specify a near-by village called Khorto. As to his dates, one tradition holds that he lived at the time of the Seljuk sultan Alā-ed-Din (Aladdin) in the thirteenth century, and another that he lived in the fourteenth to fifteenth centuries during the reigns of the early Ottoman sultans. The latter view, which enables the Hodja to be represented as coming into contact with Timur Leng or Timur 'the

Lame' (the Tamburlaine of Marlowe), has perhaps the widest currency. In the middle of the thirteenth century the Mongols destroyed the Empire of the Seljuk Turks. The beginning of the fourteenth century, however, witnessed the foundation of the Ottoman dynasty by Othman I, and under his successor, Orkhan I, Turkey was firmly established as a great power. In 1400, however, the Mongols again invaded Anatolia or Asiatic Turkey under Timur's leadership, and the Ottoman Turks were defeated at the Battle of Ankara in 1402. Timur Leng retired from the region in 1403, but while he was in Turkey, according to tradition, he stayed near Ak-Shehir, where he made the acquaintance of Nasreddin Hodja. What sort of a man Timur was may be judged from the account of his week in the country related below (p. 48). He struck fear into the Turks, and the many tales in which the Hodja is represented as making a fool of the terrible conqueror are, like so many Oriental tales, wish-fulfilment phantasies. Perhaps the most famous anecdote linking the two is that in which Timur and Hodja are together in the *hammām* or Turkish baths. Timur asks the Hodja what he thinks he, the Conqueror of the World, is worth. The Hodja replies, '*50 akches.*' 'How can that be?' says Timur. 'The bath-robe I am wearing is worth *50 akches!*' 'Yes,' said the Hodja, 'that is what I was pricing.' This reply, implying that the Conqueror, stripped of all his pomp, was worth nothing, reverberated round the Eastern world as Diogenes' remark to Alexander the Great that the greatest gift he could give him would be to stand out of his light did around the Western world. In another story Timur, with some justification, tells the Hodja, who is sitting near him: 'It is evident that you are not far removed from a donkey!' 'No,' replies the Hodja, 'only a couple of yards' (p. 82). The Ottoman Sultan Bayazid could do nothing to Timur but, at least in the imagination of his much-suffering subjects, the Hodja could twist his tail.

Stories that are now attached to the Hodja were formerly told about an Arab called Djuhā who is mentioned by Persian writers as early as the eleventh century, and it may be that *Hodja* is a corruption of his name, i.e. the rendering of an unfamiliar name by a familiar title. The words and deeds of Djuhā were quoted by the thirteenth-century Persian mystic, Djelāl-ad-Din Rūmī, as illustrations of his philosophy, just as a modern philosopher might quote *Alice in Wonderland*. Whatever the ultimate origin of some of the Nasreddin Hodja stories —India, Greece, Syria, Arabia (and as in the case of ordinary folk-tales, ultimate origins are extremely difficult to determine)—many

3

probably entered Turkey from Persia, the cultural importance of which has already been referred to above. A possible answer to the question as to whether Nasreddin Hodja existed or not is, 'yes, many times over', for like Till Uilenspiegel of the Low Countries, for example, he was probably made the hero of many a funny remark or action which occurred or was imagined to have occurred in his people's surroundings. The main criterion now for the inclusion of a story in the Nasreddin Hodja canon seems to be that it is funny, as far as the people who relate these stories are concerned, that is, since many of our modern European *hodjas* will continue to argue about these matters. *Funny*, of course, can mean *witty* and *humorous*, and this

explains the duality of the Hodja's nature: for on some occasions he is made to say and do things which are remarkably intelligent, and on other occasions things which are remarkably stupid. The main thing is that both made people laugh. The Hodja is very Turkish, and yet his image appealed strongly to many of the Sultan's foreign subjects whose dearest wish was to throw off the Ottoman yoke. Tales of the Hodja are related with great glee among Arabs, Armenians, Greeks and Serbs, many of whom are reluctant to see any good qualities in his people. However, the Hodja was the representative of a society which was non-nationalistic, a theocratic microcosm in which, although Muhammad was the greatest and last prophet, Moses and Jesus also were venerated as prophets, and their followers, Jews, Armenians and Greeks, honoured as 'the people of The Book'. Perhaps things were not so good in practice as in theory but, after all, the Hodja was not the agent of the *Sublime Porte*. One of his functions, in fact, seems to have consisted in cocking a snook at authority, which always and everywhere appears more dignified in its own eyes than in those of people, who, in Abraham Lincoln's words, cannot be fooled all the time.

Although some of the tales which follow were made known to the English public by W. B. Barker over a hundred years ago, the Hodja has not yet taken his proper place among us beside such other humorous foreign characters as Baron Münchhausen and Till Uilenspiegel. This is a pity, for the Hodja's humour, although thoroughly Turkish, is for the most part universal. Some of the jokes, even though they may be most intimately connected with Muslim society, can be understood by outsiders: for example, the Hodja's deliberate misquotation of the Qoran on p. 46. Those that cannot be understood without a mass of explanations in the form of footnotes have been omitted from this selection. The point of many of the jokes is sharpened in the original Turkish by puns and rhymes, and these too must be forgone in an English version. But much remains. From time to time it may seem difficult to get the point of a joke. What is funny, for example, in that reproduced on p. 18: 'Thirty-two of them make a bushel' (actually the original says 'ten of them makes a *kile*', but the point of the joke is not changed by translating it into English terms)? So what? In this case the humour is not verbal; what is funny is the situation, the embarrassing anticlimax. What *could* the poor Hodja say, after all? The roots of humour go very deep, and the philosopher Bergson is very interesting on the subject. Perhaps one should beware of

5

reading *too* deeply into a joke, but the one about the cooking-pot giving birth and then dying (at least according to the Hodja's account) may seem to link up with animism, that is, the belief, shared by Victor Hugo, that everything—stones, trees, animals, and hence even a cooking-pot—has a soul. The joke may be a subconscious throw-back to the mentality of the Turks' Central Asian ancestors, and may not have seemed funny at all to a *shaman* or local witch-doctor.

...AND HIS DONKEY

Nasreddin Hodja's donkey plays as important a role in the tales as Sancho Panza's mount in *The Adventures of Don Quixote* or Robert Louis Stevenson's in *Travels with a Donkey*. Sometimes it is the subject of the joke, sometimes it acts as a foil for the Hodja's humour, and in one case, when the Hodja is engaged in a medieval disputation with three Christian monks, it seems to become a whole system of philosophy (p. 40). Before the advent of the motor-car, which has completely changed the aspect of the Middle East, and not perhaps for the better, the donkey was, apart from the feet, the main means of transport in small towns and villages, camels and horses being used for longer journeys. Even now in Turkey and the Arab countries the donkey is as common as (*anno* 1964) the red double-decker bus in London. The donkey was the Hodja's mount, and there are many tales to show that he was not at all at home on a horse, which was the mount of the upper classes, and even at one time in Turkey forbidden to non-Muslims. Sometimes the Hodja is depicted riding his donkey back to front, in one case (p. 65) allegedly so that he might maintain his proper position *vis-à-vis* his pupils. It is tempting to suggest that he rode thus because he knew where he was going but wanted to see where he had been. Alas, the truth of the matter is merely that such was the traditional riding position of the buffoon. That Nasreddin Hodja was no ordinary buffoon, however, (for usually there is method in his madness and wisdom in his folly), the following pages will show.

Note. In some of the tales mention is made of various articles of Turkish dress. The *kavuk*, or scholar's turban, has been mentioned above. The Hodja might instead wear a simple felt cap or rough woollen head-cloth when labouring in the fields, as perhaps when the studious *molla* (Muslim theologian) found him outside Ak-Shehir (p. 35). He would wear a shirt (*kamees*) and a pair of baggy trousers (*shalvar*), and over the shirt a waistcoat (*yelek*). Over these he might wear a long cloth coat called a *kaftan*, or a *binish*, or a *djübbeh*, or, in cold weather, a thick black coat called an *aba*. On the little finger of his right hand he would probably have worn a seal-ring for signing letters and other documents; and as a literary man, he would probably have worn in his girdle a brass case about nine inches long containing pens and ink, the rather cumbrous equivalent of the modern fountain-pen.

Once the Hodja borrowed a large cauldron from his neighbour, and when some time had passed, he placed a small metal coffee-can in it and took it back to its owner.

'What is that?' said the latter, pointing to the small can.

'Oh, your cauldron gave birth to that while it was in my possession.'

The neighbour was delighted, and took both the cauldron and the coffee-can.

Some days later, the Hodja again asked his neighbour to lend him his cauldron, which he did. This time a few weeks passed, and when the neighbour felt he could do without his cauldron no longer, he went to the Hodja, and asked him to return it.

'I cannot,' replied the Hodja. 'Your cauldron has died.'

'Died?' cried the neighbour. 'How can a cauldron die?'

'Where is the difficulty?' said the Hodja. 'You believed it could give birth. Why will you not believe it can die?'

9

THE Hodja was walking home when a man came up behind him and gave him a thump on the back of the head. When the Hodja turned round, the man began to apologize, saying that he had taken him for a friend of his. The Hodja, however, was very angry at this assault upon his dignity and dragged the man off to the court. It happened, however, that his assailant was a close friend of the *cadi*, and after listening to the two parties in the dispute, the *cadi* said to his friend:

'You are in the wrong. You shall pay the Hodja a farthing damages.

His friend said he had not that amount of money on him, and went off, saying he would fetch it.

Hodja waited and waited, and still the man did not return. When an hour had passed, the Hodja got up and gave the *cadi* a mighty thump on the back of his head.

'I can wait no longer,' he said. 'When he comes, the farthing is yours.'

ONE day Nasreddin Hodja returned from the bazaar with a choice piece of lamb. He gave it to his wife, and with visions of the tasty dinner he would later enjoy, went back to the bazaar to drink coffee and smoke a pipe. As soon as his back was turned, however, his wife chopped up the meat, stuck the pieces on skewers, and then invited her friends round to partake of her *shish-kebab*. Not long after the ladies had departed, the Hodja returned. He was disappointed to see nothing but a bowl of thin soup placed before him.

'Where is the meat I brought back from the bazaar?' he asked.

'The cat ate it,' replied his wife.

'How much did it weigh, about?' said the Hodja.

'About an *okka* (2¾ pounds),' said his wife.

The cat was very small. The Hodja went to the kitchen, took a pair of scales, picked up the cat, and weighed it.

'Exactly one *okka*,' he announced. 'Strange! If this is the cat, where is the meat? If this is the meat, where is the cat?'

10

ONE night a thief entered the Hodja's house.

'Effendi,' whispered his wife, 'there is a thief in the next room!'

'Hush!' said the Hodja. 'Wait. Perhaps he will find something worth taking. Then we can easily take it from him.'

THE Hodja was once asked how old he was.

'Forty,' he said.

Ten years passed, and someone else asked him how old he was.

'Forty,' he said.

Some of those who had witnessed his answer ten years before were present on this occasion.

'When you were asked ten years ago how old you were,' they objected, 'you said "forty" then.'

'That is correct,' said the Hodja. 'A man must not go back on his word.'

A neighbour one day asked the Hodja if he might borrow his ass.

'It isn't here,' said the Hodja.

At that moment his ass brayed from behind the house.

'Effendi,' said the neighbour reproachfully, 'you said your ass was not here, and I can hear it braying.'

'May Allah forgive your lack of faith,' said the Hodja, shaking his head. 'You will believe an ass, and the word of a man whose beard is white you will not believe!'

ONE summer afternoon the Hodja was asleep on the verandah when he dreamed that a stranger promised him ten pieces of gold. The stranger placed them into the Hodja's palm one by one until he reached the tenth piece, with which he seemed hesitant to part.

'What are you waiting for?' said the Hodja. 'You promised me ten.'

At that very moment he woke up, and saw that his palm was empty. He quickly shut his eyes again, and stretched out his hand.

'All right,' he said, 'I'll settle for nine!'

11

ONE evening the Hodja said to his wife:

'If it rains tomorrow, I shall collect firewood in the forest. If it is dry, I shall plough the field.'

'Say *inshallah* (if God wills) like a good Muslim!' said his wife.

'Why?' said the Hodja, rebelliously. 'Either it will rain or it will not rain, and I have decided on how to act in either contingency.'

The next day it was not raining and the Hodja set off to plough his field. On the way he met a band of soldiers.

'Hey, uncle!' they cried. 'How do we get to such-and-such a village?'

'I can't remember,' said the Hodja, who could not be bothered to explain.

'Well, let us see if this will make you remember!' said the soldiers, and they began to belabour him with their sticks.

'I remember now,' said the Hodja.

'Then you can lead us there,' said the soldiers.

On the way it began to rain, and by the time he had led the soldiers to their destination, he was wet through, muddy and footsore. It was midnight before he crawled back home and knocked on the door.

'Who is that?' called his wife.

'It is I,' said the Hodja, '*inshallah!*'

12

THE Hodja lost his donkey and went to look for it. As he walked along the road, he was loud in his praises of Allah.

'I understand that you have lost your donkey,' said a passer-by. 'Why, then, are you praising God?'

'I thank God that I was not on it when it disappeared,' replied the Hodja.

He went on his way, and changed his prayer for a merry song.

'What are you singing for?' asked another. 'When one loses one's donkey there is more cause for tears than laughter.'

'There's still a hope that my donkey is on the other side of that hill in front of me,' said the Hodja. 'But if I don't find him there, you will soon see I can howl!'

By the afternoon the Hodja had still not found his donkey, and he had notices put up in all the coffee-houses that whoever found his donkey could keep it, and he would give him saddle and bridle as well.

'What sense is there in that, Hodja?' asked a friend. 'Now even if the donkey is found, it will no longer belong to you. What good can it do you?'

'Have you never heard of the great pleasure that finding something gives?' said the Hodja.

ONE night the Hodja looked out of the window and saw a large figure of a man standing in the garden in the moonlight, his arms out stretched wide.

He hurriedly woke his wife.

'Bring me my bow and arrows,' he said. 'There is some dangerous fellow in our garden.'

He drew back his bow and loosed off an arrow.

The arrow hit the apparition right in the belly.

'That will teach you to meddle with me,' said the Hodja, proudly. But he was afraid to go out into the garden all the same.

'We shall leave him until the morning,' he said.

The next day he went out into the garden, and saw an arrow sticking out of his robe, which was hanging on the line. His wife had washed it the previous day and hung it on the line to dry.

The Hodja fell on his knees, and began to give loud thanks to God.

'Why are you praying so fervently?' asked his wife.

'Can you not see, woman?' he said. 'My arrow went right through the middle of my robe. What would have happened to me if, but for the mercy of Allah, I had been wearing it at the time?'

T̲HE Hodja and his wife were sleeping peacefully when, around midnight, the sound of angry voices rose from the street.

The Hodja woke up and wanted to know what the quarrel was about. His wife told him that it was no concern of his, and that he should go back to sleep.

But the Hodja would not listen, and wrapping himself up in his blanket, he went downstairs and out on to the street.

As soon as the Hodja appeared before them, the two men stopped quarrelling, grabbed his blanket and ran off down the street with it.

The Hodja returned ruefully to the bedroom.

'Well, what were they quarrelling for?' asked his wife.

'They were quarrelling for my blanket,' said the Hodja. 'No sooner had they set eyes on it, than their dispute came to an end.'

O̲NE day the Hodja picked up a spade and began to dig a deep hole in his garden.

His neighbour came up and asked him what he was doing.

'You and the others have been wondering for some time what to do with the earth that is lying at the side of the road after the repairs done to it. Well, I am digging a hole to bury it in.

'But Hodja,' said the other, 'where will you put the earth you are digging out of the hole?'

'Oh, come now!' said the Hodja. 'I cannot attend to every detail.

ONE day, in the course of a sermon he was giving on the mercies of the All High, the Hodja raised up his eyes to Heaven, and cried:

'Give thanks to Allah, O Muslims, who in His wisdom has not provided the camel with wings. If he had, the roofs of our houses would all come crashing down upon us!'

ONE Friday Nasreddin Hodja mounted the *mimbar* or pulpit in the mosque of Ak-Shehir to give the sermon.

'O true believers, do you know what I am going to talk to you about today?' he asked.

The congregation looked at each other in some surprise, then shook their heads.

'We have no idea,' they said.

'If you have no idea,' said the Hodja, 'what is the use of my talking to you?'

With that he descended from the *mimbar* and went home.

The following Friday he entered the mosque, mounted the *mimbar* and again asked the congregation:

'O true believers, do you know what I am going to talk to you about today?'

'Yes,' said the wily ones.

'Well, if you already know,' said the Hodja, 'what is the use of my telling you?'

And again he descended from the *mimbar* and went home.

When he again entered the mosque, he mounted the *mimbar*, and asked the same question:

'O true believers, do you know what I am going to talk to you about today?'

The congregation had long since prepared their reply.

'Some of us do, and some of us do not,' they said.

'In that case,' said the Hodja, 'let those who do tell those who do not.'

And away he went.

ONE day the Hodja was hunting in the forest when he caught a hare. He had never seen a hare before in his life, so he put it in his bag, tied up the top, and went home.

'Wife,' he said, 'do not touch this bag. There is something in here that I have never seen before in my life. I just do not know what it is. I am going out to fetch the doctor and the judge to see if they know what to make of it.'

And off he went.

The more his wife thought about what was in the bag, the more curious she became. Finally, she could bear it no longer. She carefully undid the string and looked inside. Out jumped the hare, through the window, across the garden, over the field and into the woods. When she had recovered from her shock, the Hodja's wife began to worry about what her husband would say when he saw that his mysterious object had disappeared. So she took a metal quart-sized can for measuring corn, put it in the bag, tied it up, and acted as though nothing had happened.

Her husband had found the doctor and the judge and a few other friends, and had told them what a mysterious thing he had found in the woods, a thing he had never seen before in all his life, and he was over fifty. Agog with excitement and curiosity, they entered the kitchen. The Hodja carefully undid the string, and turned the bag upside down.

'Psst! Psst!' he said.

Out fell the quart measure.

For a while there was an astonished silence. Then the Hodja said:

'Thirty-two of those make a bushel.'

ONCE in the course of a very cold winter the Hodja's friends proposed a wager.

'If you stand all night on the village square, and do not move, and do not try to warm yourself by artificial means, we shall stand you a dinner. If you fail to do so, you will stand us one.'

'All right,' said the Hodja.

And all night he stood among the snow and frost. When morning came, he rushed triumphantly to his friends.

'I have won the wager,' he said.

'Tell us what happened,' they replied.

'I stood still all night on the village square. I nearly froze from the cold, but nothing happened.'

'Nothing at all?' asked the friends.

'Well, at about midnight I did see a candle burn in a window about three miles away.'

'Then you have lost!' cried his friends. 'You warmed yourself by that candle.'

They would not listen to the Hodja's protests, and he was compelled to invite them that evening to a dinner at his house.

They arrived full of good humour and expectations. They waited and waited, however, and still no food was placed on the table. After about three hours, when the Hodja had gone into the yard, they decided to look in the kitchen to see if a dinner really was being prepared, and there they saw a gigantic cauldron suspended over the tiny flame of a candle.

'Hodja! What is this?' they cried. 'How do you expect such a tiny flame to boil such a large pot?'

'You forced me to conclude that it was possible,' said the Hodja. 'If I was kept warm in the village square by the light of a candle three miles away, surely the same flame will boil a kettle only three inches away!'

W HEN the Hodja exercised the function of *khātib* or preacher in Sivri-Hisar, he had a quarrel with the *muhtar* (mayor). It so happened that very shortly afterwards the *muhtar* up and died.

The townspeople came to fetch the Hodja.

'The *muhtar* is dead,' they said. 'Come and read the prayer for the dead over him.'

'What would be the use?' said the Hodja. 'We have had a quarrel, and he will not listen to me!'

Oᴎᴇ day the Hodja and his son went on a short journey, the boy seated on the donkey. On the way they met some people coming in the opposite direction.

'That's modern youth for you,' they said. 'The son rides on a donkey and lets his poor old father walk!'

When they had gone, the boy insisted that his father take his place on the donkey. The Hodja mounted the donkey, and his son walked at his side. They met some more people.

'Just look at that!' they said. 'There is a full-grown man riding on the donkey, while his poor little son has to walk!'

'The best thing to do,' said Nasreddin, when they had disappeared from sight, 'is for both of us to walk. Then there can be no such arguments.'

So they continued their way walking beside the donkey. It was not long before they met another group.

'Just look at those fools,' they said, pointing to the Hodja and his son. 'They plod along in the heat of the sun, and their donkey takes it easy!'

'You will have learned, my boy,' said the Hodja, when they had gone, 'just how difficult it is to escape the criticism of wagging tongues!'

In the coffee-shop they began to talk about horse-riding.

'I remember once,' said the Hodja, 'that in my youth a man produced a horse that nobody had managed to break in. As soon as anyone sat upon its back, it bucked so much that it sent him flying. Many of the young men in the village tried to mount it, but in vain. Finally, they asked me to try. I was young and sturdy in those days. I tucked up my skirts, rolled up my sleeves, grasped the horse by its mane, and leapt on to its back.'

Just at that moment a man entered the coffee-shop who had been present on that occasion.

'Yes, yes! Go on!' said the Hodja's friends, all agog.

'It sent me flying,' he said.

Two men who were involved in an argument appealed to the Hodja to settle it for them. The first man gave his version of the quarrel, and when he had listened attentively to all he had to say, the Hodja nodded his head, and said:

'You are right.'

'It is not like that at all!' exclaimed the second man, and began to relate his side of the story to the Hodja. When he had finished, the Hodja said:

'You are right.'

The Hodja's wife, who had listened to everything, could bear it no longer.

'Hodja,' she said, 'they cannot both be right!'

The Hodja thought for a minute.

'Wife, you are right, too!' he said.

One day the Hodja looked out of the window and saw a money-lender, to whom he owed a large sum, coming towards the house.

22

'Wife!' he said. 'Here comes the money-lender. Don't open the door. Tell him what I have told you to tell him through the window.'

The money-lender knocked on the door, and Nasreddin's wife stuck her head out of the window.

'What do you want?' she said.

'I should have thought you would have known by now,' said the other. 'I have come for the money you owe me.'

'My husband is a little short of money at present,' said the Hodja's wife, 'but he has thought of a good scheme which will enable him to pay you back. At the back of our house there is a large thorn-bush. The shepherds drive their sheep along the lane and some of the wool catches on the thorns. My husband plans to collect this wool, and sell it to pay you back.'

The money-lender, realizing that under such a scheme it would take him about a thousand years to get his money back, could not help throwing back his head and roaring with laughter.

When the Hodja heard this, he grew very angry, and thrust his head over his wife's shoulder.

'Yes, you're happy now!' he exclaimed. 'You see that you have placed your money in good hands, and are jumping for joy!'

W HEN he was in Konya, Nasreddin visited the district judge and asked him to make him *cadi* somewhere. All the vacancies had been filled, however, and the judge could not grant his request But he was disposed to give the Hodja an honorary title, and asked him for suggestions.

'Make me then a "shadow-*cadi*",' said the Hodja.

'What would be the function of such an office?' said the judge.

'Just send me the cases you cannot yourself decide,' said the Hodja.

He stationed himself in a corner of the court and waited.

One day two men appeared before the judge.

'Effendi,' said the plaintiff, 'this man refuses to pay me my due. He was walking along with a bundle of firewood on his back when he stumbled and fell, and I offered to carry it for him. When I asked him what he would give me if I did so, he replied "Nothing". I carried the wood to his house for him, and when I asked for my wages, he did not give me "Nothing". I have brought him to court to make him pay me.'

The judge was perplexed by this strange request, and sent the men to the 'shadow-*cadi*'.

The Hodja listened to the plaintiff's story, then said:

'Do you see that small carpet before my desk? Lift it up.'

The man did so.

'What is under it?' asked the Hodja.

'Nothing,'said the man.

'That's your wages,' said the Hodja. 'Take it and go!'

A man once brought the Hodja a letter he had received and asked
him to read it for him.

'The handwriting is too bad,' said the Hodja. 'I cannot read it.'

The man grew angry.

'You call yourself a Hodja,' he cried, 'and wear the turban of a
learned man, and you cannot even read a letter!'

The Hodja took off his *kavuk* and placed it before him.

'If you think that everyone who wears a turban like this is a learned
man,' he said, 'you put it on, and see if *you* can read the letter!'

ONE day in Ak-Shehir the *imām* was washing his hands in a large fountain, when he slipped and fell in. As he was floundering about, a large number of people gathered round and tried to help him.

'Give us your hand, effendi!' they cried.

The *imām* took no notice and tried, in vain, to climb up the steep walls of the fountain by himself.

The Hodja was standing at the edge of the crowd.

'You will not help a man of religion that way,' he muttered. 'They will give you nothing, but will take everything.'

And pushing his way through the crowd, he stretched out his hand to the *imām*, and said:

'Take my hand, effendi!'

The *imām* took the Hodja's hand and was pulled to safety—without, however, knowing what he had thereby proved.

A man saw the Hodja, who was very hungry, dipping his right hand into the rice, instead of the first two fingers and the thumb, as etiquette demanded.

'Why are you eating with five fingers, effendi?' he asked.

'Because I have not got six,' said the Hodja.

ONE evening the *cadi* of Sivri-Hisar got very drunk, and stumbling into a copse at the side of the road, flung off his *djübbeh* and turban, and went to sleep half-naked under a tree.

Nasreddin Hodja chanced to pass by a little later with his pupil Ahmet. He picked up the finely embroidered *djübbeh* and the turban, and took them home.

When the *cadi* finally came to his senses, he noticed that his clothes had gone, and arriving home, he ordered his servants to search the town for them.

The following day the Hodja was found walking around in the *cadi's* cloak, and was forthwith brought before the court, presided over by his victim.

'Do you claim that that *djübbeh* is your own?' asked the *cadi*.

'No, effendi,' replied the Hodja.

'Then what is it doing in your possession?'

'Effendi,' said the Hodja, 'I was walking on the outskirts of the town yesterday evening with my pupil Ahmet, when we came across a sight abhorrent to all Muslims. Some fellow had got himself dead drunk, and was snoring away under a tree, half naked. Fearing that robbers would take advantage of his helpless and sinful condition, I took the *djübbeh* and turban he had flung aside in his lack of self-control. If he can be found, I should like to return him his property.'

'Who knows what rascal it was, to make such a spectacle of himself!' muttered the *cadi*. 'I want nothing more to do with this matter!'

And dismissing the Hodja, he breathed a silent good-bye to his cloak and turban.

WHEN the Hodja was a young boy, there lived near him a most self-assured boy whose constant boast it was that no one could trick him.

'Stay here a while,' said the Hodja to him one day, 'and I'll find a way to trick you.'

The Hodja went off.

Three hours later the boy was still waiting for his return.

'What are you waiting for?' asked a passer-by.

'I have been waiting for Nasreddin to find a way to trick me,' said the boy. 'I have been waiting here for three hours, and he has still not returned.'

'What more do you want then?' said the other. 'How much longer are you going to stand there?'

THE Hodja was returning home one night with his pupil Imad when he saw a gang of thieves standing in front of a house, trying to break the lock.

The Hodja decided that if he said anything he would probably get hurt. So he said nothing, and passed by.

His pupil, however, had not understood what was going on.

'Why are all those men standing there?' he said.

'Shush!' said the Hodja. 'They are playing the rebāb.'

'But I cannot hear any music!' protested Imad.

'We shall hear the music tomorrow,' said the Hodja.

ONE day the Hodja was sitting at the side of the sea when he felt very thirsty. He dipped his hands into the sea and drank the water. Far from quenching his thirst, of course, it made him thirstier than ever, and he walked away from the coast until he found a fresh spring.

When he had quenched his thirst, he filled his *kavuk* with the water, returned to the sea, and tipped it in.

'You froth and foam and make a great noise for nothing,' he said. 'Now see what real water tastes like!'

ONCE the Hodja had business in Bursa, which was the Ottoman capital before the capture of Constantinople. For some reason the Hodja could not bring his affairs to a successful conclusion, and an acquaintance advised him to pray in the large and famous mosque called Ulu Djami.

'If you say morning prayers for forty days in succession in front of the *mihrāb*, and then pray fervently on the forty-first morning for your wish to be granted, it will be.'

The Hodja carried out these instructions to the letter, and nothing at all came of it.

A few days afterwards he entered a small mosque near the great Ulu Djami called the Orhan Djamii, and prayed that his wish be granted.

That same day brought his affairs to a very successful conclusion indeed.

Then the Hodja entered the Ulu Djami, and cried out in a loud voice:

'You ought to be ashamed of yourself, great mosque!' he said. 'Your little son has done what you couldn't do!'

ONCE during a long journey with the caravan, the Hodja, so as not to get lost, attached an aubergine to his belt; thus he would be recognizable to all. One night, however, when they were sleeping in the caravanserai, a practical joker removed the aubergine from the Hodja's belt, and tied it to his own. When the Hodja awoke, he saw the other man before him with his aubergine in his belt.

He was puzzled.

'That is me there,' he said. 'But—who am I here?'

ONE day the Hodja decided he was tired of feeding his donkey, and asked his wife to go and feed it instead. She refused, however, saying that that was his work. In the end they agreed that whichever one of them spoke first, that one should go and feed the donkey.

The Hodja retired forthwith to a corner and sat in it without saying a word. His wife became fed up with the tense atmosphere in the house, and went out to visit a neighbour. Once there, of course, she could not keep silent, and she related what had happened.

'He is such a stubborn mule!' she said. 'He'll die of hunger rather than speak.'

'I will send him some soup,' said her friend, and she poured some out in a plate and sent her son to take it to the Hodja.

In the meantime, however, a thief, hearing no sound from inside the Hodja's house, entered quietly and began to stuff everything of value into his sack. Eventually he walked into the room where the Hodja was sitting, and was almost frightened out of his life. As the Hodja made no sound or move, however, he came to the conclusion that he was paralysed, and added to his collection of valuable objects under the very eyes of their owner. The Hodja was furious, but thought that if he moved, he would be bound to say something. The thief, as thorough as he was impertinent, thought it would be a pity to leave the

30

Hodja's *kavuk* behind, and carefully removed it from his head. Then he left.

Five minutes afterwards, the boy arrived with the plate of soup. The Hodja, deciding that, after all, he ought to make an attempt to have the thief apprehended, tried to tell the boy in gestures what had happened so that he should fetch the police. The boy understood nothing. When the Hodja tried to describe how the thief had taken his hat from his very head, he waved his hand three times round his head and then pointed to it. The boy thought he had understood what the Hodja wanted, and making three circular movements with the plate of soup over the Hodja's head, he tipped the hot contents on to his skull.

Whatever the Hodja thought, he still said nothing.

The boy went back home, and told his mother and the Hodja's wife everything he had seen—how the cupboards and trunks were wide open, vases overturned, and how the place seemed to contain much less than when he last went there with his mother. He also related how the Hodja tried to eat his soup through the top of his head.

'There must be something wrong!' said the Hodja's wife, and she hurried home as fast as her legs would take her. When she entered the house, she was, for a moment, truly speechless. Then,

'Merciful God! What has happened?' she cried.

'I've won! I've won!' rejoiced the Hodja. 'You feed the donkey!'

Then he remembered the thief.

'But just look what trouble your obstinacy has caused!' he said.

How can one attain wisdom?' the Hodja was once asked.

'Always listen attentively to what those who know tell you,' he replied. 'And if someone is listening to you, listen carefully to what you are saying.'

WHEN the three holy months of Redjeb, Shaban and Ramazan began, the Hodja, as was the custom of the holy men, went round the countryside to collect alms and to find an appointment as *imam* in one of the villages during the Ramazan fast. Wherever he went, however, they told him that they already had arranged for an *imam*, and gave the Hodja nothing.

When he arrived at the seventh village, he found that it was the scene of great excitement. For the past few months a fox had been causing great losses among the chickens, geese and turkeys of the neighbourhood, and finally the angry farmers had caught it in a trap. Filled with the spirit of revenge, they were vying with each other in suggestions as to what dire death the fox should die. At this moment the Hodja arrived, and the villagers turned to him for advice.

'Leave it to me,' said the Hodja, and seeing his white beard and his confident air, the villagers entrusted the fate of the fox to him.

The Hodja led the fox some distance away. He took off his cloak and his scholar's head-dress, and put them on the fox. Then he patted it on the back, and let it go.

The furious villagers, seeing their enemy making for the fields at great speed, rushed up.

'What have you done?' they cried.

'Do not worry,' replied the Hodja. 'I have inflicted the greatest possible punishment on the fox. Anyone who sees him will take him for a scholar, and then may Allah help him, for he will starve to death within the week!'

WHEN still a little boy, the Hodja visited Ak-Shehir, a town much bigger than his birth-place of Sivri-Hisar. In his village the mosque was very small, while that in Ak-Shehir had a large dome and a tall minaret. As he passed by, the Hodja heard the muezzin calling the faithful to prayer, but misunderstood the significance of his loud cries.

He looked up.

'I cannot help you, uncle,' he called. 'If you had got stuck up a tree, there would have been branches for me to hold on to. But that smooth tower I cannot climb!'

THE Hodja was digging in his cellar when his spade went through the wall. Looking through the hole he had made, he saw a herd of cows, but did not realize that he was looking into his neighbour's cowshed.

He dropped his spade and ran quickly upstairs.

'Wife,' he cried, in great excitement. 'I have found a cave in our cellar full of cows dating from the time of Diocletian!'

(Note: This may be an echo of the legend of the Seven Sleepers of Ephesus, who took refuge in a cave during the Roman Emperor Diocletian's persecution of the Christians (303-311) and who woke up hundreds of years later. They are the prototype of Rip Van Winkle.)

THE Hodja was walking in a cemetery when he slipped and fell into a newly dug grave. Collecting his wits at the bottom of the pit, he said to himself:

'Let us pretend to be a corpse, and see whether the angels Munker and Nekir will come and question me!'

He was already carried away by his imagination, when he heard the sound of bells, and great clinking and clanking, the sound of hoofs, the crack of whips, and a great shouting and hullabaloo.

33

The noise was caused by five mules laden with crockery which were being driven past the cemetery by their drovers, who were in a great hurry, and very bad-tempered.

The Hodja did not know this, of course, and thought that the end of the world had come.

For a moment he did not know what to do, but suddenly decided that he might as well make a dash for it. So out of the grave he clambered, and off into the road. Not looking where he was going, he ran straight into the mules, which stopped dead, reared on their hind legs, and colliding one with the other, smashed their load of cups, glasses, jugs and dishes to smithereens. The drovers were furious.

'Who are you?' they shouted to Nasreddin. 'What are you running around like a madman for?'

'I am a corpse,' said the Hodja. 'I dwell in the other world, and have just come out to have a look round.'

Alas, the most imaginative lies are not always believed.

'We'll give you a look round!' cried the drovers, and raising their whips, they began to beat the poor Hodja all over.

It was late at night by the time the Hodja, feeling very sorry for himself, dragged his bruised and weary bones home.

'Where have you been till this hour?' said his wife.

'I fell into a grave, down among the dead men,' said the Hodja, 'right into the other world.'

'Oh? What is it like in the other world?' asked his wife, greatly interested.

'It is nothing special,' sighed the Hodja. 'But let me give you a bit of advice if you go there—do not have anything to do with mules laden with crockery!'

ONE day, for a joke, they asked the Hodja:
'When there is a new moon, what do they do with the old one?'
The Hodja did not want to admit his ignorance.
'They cut it up and make it into stars,' he replied.

A *molla*, a learned Muslim theologian, was travelling the country in search of knowledge, meeting scholars and interrogating them on various philosophical problems.

One day, when he had asked rather a difficult question, his informant said:

'There is only one person likely to be able to give you an answer to that. He is Nasreddin Hodja of Ak-Shehir.'

So the *molla* made his way towards Ak-Shehir. On the outskirts of the town he saw a peasant ploughing a field, dressed in a coarse *aba*, with an old felt cap on his head, and old leather sandals on his feet.

It was the Hodja, but the *molla* did not know this.

Feeling in need of a little rest, he thought he would try his questions on the peasant. Who knows, after all, what wisdom sometimes emerges from the mouths of fools?

The Hodja himself had his eyes on the fine, round, red pomegranates the stranger was carrying with him, and when the *molla* said he wished to pose him a few questions, he said:

'Give me a pomegranate for each answer, and I shall solve your problems.'

The theologian put his questions, and was surprised to find that the peasant was never lost for an answer. The pomegranates, therefore, were soon exhausted. When the last one had joined its fellows at the Hodja's feet, the *molla* said:

'I have one more question on which I should value your opinion.'

'Have you any more pomegranates in that bag?' asked the Hodja.

'No,' replied the other.

'Then please do not waste my time,' said the Hodja. 'I have work to do.'

And thus saying, he got up and continued his ploughing.

'Ah!' sighed the *molla*. 'If that is the quality of the peasants of these parts, the scholars will make an even greater fool of me.'

And he gave Ak-Shehir a miss.

ONE night a thief stole the Hodja's donkey. When he told his friends of his loss next morning, they were very critical.

'Why did you not put a lock on the stable door?' they said. 'Why did you not wake up when the thief came in?'

'Do you not think the thief is a little to blame too?' said the Hodja.

ONE morning, at the hour of the dawn prayer, the Hodja called out aloud:

'Lord, give me a thousand pieces of gold. If you give me nine hundred and ninety-nine pieces, I shall not accept them!'

And he continued to pray thus every day.

His neighbour, an infidel merchant, heard this fervent but peculiar prayer every morning, and such was his curiosity to know whether the Hodja would in fact keep his word that he placed nine hundred and ninety-nine pieces of gold in a bag, and the next morning, when the Hodja repeated his prayer, he threw the bag down the chimney, and looked in at the window to see what would happen.

The Hodja picked up the sack, counted out the nine hundred and ninety-nine pieces of gold, and said:

'Allah, who has given me nine hundred and ninety-nine pieces of gold, will surely give me another one before long!'

The odds against the Hodja acquiring his thousand gold pieces had clearly shortened. He had, after all, not said that God should give them to him all at once.

The infidel, seeing the Hodja determined to keep the pieces of gold, waited until it was quite light, and then went to see the Hodja.

'Effendi,' he said, 'a joke is a joke. Give me back my golden coins.'

'Are you mad, merchant?' said the Hodja. 'When have I borrowed money from you?'

'You know what I mean,' said the infidel. 'Hearing your prayer and wondering if you would be true to your word, I threw a sack containing nine hundred and ninety-nine gold coins down your chimney this morning.'

'Do you think I shall believe that you were willing to risk the loss of such a large sum just for the pleasure of tempting a true believer?' said the Hodja. 'The coins are mine. Allah gave them to me as a reward for sincere and steadfast prayers.'

'I shall take you to court for this,' said the infidel. 'The coins are mine!'

'I am quite prepared to submit to the judgment of the court,' said the Hodja, 'but I am not so young any more, and do not feel up to

making the journey on foot.'

The infidel ran quickly off, and returned with a sturdy mule, and offered to lend it to the Hodja for the journey.

'I am, after all, a man of some position in society,' said the Hodja. 'I cannot appear before the *cadi* in this old *djübbeh* of mine.'

The infidel was determined that no excuse the Hodja might bring forward should prevent his appearing in court, and he went indoors, and returned with a fine silk robe, and a sumptuous fur coat.

'I'll lend you these for the occasion,' he said, 'but let us hurry.'

The Hodja put the clothes on, mounted the mule, and they set off.

'What is the matter?' said the *cadi*, when they arrived before him.

'This man has nine hundred and ninety-nine coins belonging to me,' said the infidel, 'and refuses to return them.'

And he told the judge the whole story.

'Effendi,' said the Hodja, 'this man is my neighbour. He must have heard me counting out the nine hundred and ninety-nine coins which God gave me in answer to my prayer, and now claims them to be his own.'

'They are mine,' said the infidel.

38

'Effendi!' said the Hodja. 'No doubt he will soon be saying that the very mule I am riding belongs to him also.'

'It *is* mine!' cried the infidel.

'You see, effendi?' said the Hodja. 'And no doubt he will even go so far as to say that the very clothes I am wearing on my back belong to him!'

'They *are* mine!' cried the infidel. 'Both the *djübbeh* and the fur coat.'

The judge grew very angry.

'Away with you, you rogue!' he exclaimed. 'Not only do you wish to appropriate the property of a man much honoured in our community, you are trying to make a fool of me as well!'

And he drove the infidel out of his court.

When the Hodja arrived home, he saw the infidel sitting very despondently in his house. He invited him over, and returning to him his mule, his robe, his fur coat, and his sack of gold coins, he said:

'Take your property, merchant. But do not in future try to tempt honest Muslims to break their word!'

THERE were once three learned Christian monks travelling through Turkey in search of wisdom. When they asked the Sultan about his most learned men, he jokingly referred to Nasreddin Hodja of Ak-Shehir, and the monks asked to make his acquaintance, saying that they wished to dispute with him. They each had a question to put to him.

The Hodja answered the Sultan's summons, and rode to court on his donkey.

'Let them ask their questions,' he said, when the reason for his presence was explained to him.

The first monk stepped up.

'Effendi,' he said, 'where is the centre of the earth?'

'The centre of the earth is now under the front right foot of my donkey,' replied the Hodja.

'How can you prove that?' asked the monk.

'You have only to take a tape and measure the earth,' said the Hodja. 'If you think my calculations are incorrect, tell me by how much, and we shall discuss it.'

The first monk withdrew.

The second monk stepped up.

'How many stars are there in the vault of Heaven?' he asked.

'As many as there are hairs on my donkey,' replied the Hodja.

'How can you prove that?' said the monk.

'You have only to count them,' said the Hodja. 'If you think I am wrong, tell me by how much, and we shall discuss it.'

'Effendi,' protested the monk, 'how can one count all the hairs on a donkey?'

'As easily as one can count the stars in the sky,' said the Hodja.

The second monk withdrew in some confusion.

The third monk stepped forward. He had decided to teach the Hodja a lesson, him and his counting of hairs.

'How many hairs have I in my beard?' he said.

'As many as my donkey has in his tail,' said the Hodja.

'How can you prove that?' said the third monk.

'That is not so difficult,' said the Hodja. 'We can pluck out the hairs

40

of your beard and my donkey's tail one by one. For every one of the donkey's we shall pull out one of yours. Then you will see I am right.'

The third monk was not keen to put this to the test. He acknowledged that he and his companions had been defeated in disputation, and all three were converted to Islam.

ONCE when the Hodja was acting as *cadi*, one man accused another of biting him in the ear.

'It is a lie!' said the accused. 'He bit himself in the ear!'

'Come back later,' said the Hodja, 'and I shall give my verdict.'

Thereupon he retired to his chamber, and began to experiment to see whether a man could in fact bite himself in the ear. While he was jerking his head round in an attempt to catch his ear between his teeth, he lost his balance, and falling heavily, cracked his skull.

When the two litigants returned, the plaintiff said:

'Well, effendi, can a man bite his own ear?'

'Worse!' said the Hodja. 'A man can even crack his own skull!'

THE Hodja was sitting up a tree cutting wood. A passer-by observed that the Hodja was sawing away at the branch upon which he was sitting between himself and the tree.

'You will fall down if you continue like that!' he called up.

The Hodja shrugged his shoulders, took no notice, and carried on. Suddenly the branch creaked and cracked, and the Hodja fell with a thud to the ground.

Jumping up, he ran after the man as fast as his bruises would allow him. Catching him up, he said:

'I see you are a prophet, effendi. If you knew when I should fall off a tree, you will know when I shall die.'

The stranger, not wishing to go into a long rigmarole of explanations for a man who had proved he could not see sense, cut matters very short by saying:

'When your donkey brays once, half of your soul will leave your body. When it brays for the second time, you will die!'

The Hodja, much chastened, returned to his donkey, loaded it with the firewood he had cut, and began to make his way home.

On the way, his donkey brayed. The Hodja felt very, very ill. Then the donkey brayed a second time.

'I am dead!' cried Nasreddin, and lying down on the road, he shut his eyes.

After a little time, a group of villagers passed by. Seeing the pale and prostrate Hodja, they fetched a rough wooden coffin, and started to carry him towards his house. On the way through the forest, they came to a fork in the road, and not knowing which branch to take, they began to argue.

The Hodja, already put out by the jostling he had received in the uncomfortable coffin and very much disappointed with his eternal rest, could bear it no longer.

He lifted up his head.

'When I was alive,' he snapped, 'I took the left fork!'

ONE day the Hodja arrived in Sivri-Hisar very hungry, but with no money in his pocket. As he passed by a shop in the bazaar, the delicious smell of newly baked bread wafted past his nostrils.

'Those crisp brown loaves, which smell like the bread of Paradise, are they yours?' he asked the baker.

'Yes, they are mine,' the baker said.

'And those shiny, honey-coloured, beautifully rounded rolls, as soft as the skin of a houri in heaven, fit for the prophet Muhammad himself, may Allah's blessing be upon him,' said the Hodja, hoping that the baker would finally take the hint, 'are they yours?'

'Yes, they are mine,' said the baker.

'Then what are you waiting for?' said the Hodja, angrily. 'If they are yours, eat them!'

A poor man was passing through Ak-Shehir with only a piece of dry bread between himself and starvation. As he passed by an eating-house, he saw some very appetizing meat-balls frying in a pan over the charcoal fire, and carried away by the delicious smell, he held his piece of dry bread over the pan in the hope of capturing some of it. Then he ate his bread, which seemed to taste better. The restaurant owner, however, had seen what was going on, and seizing the man by the scruff of the neck, dragged him off before the *cadi*, who at this time happened to be Nasreddin Hodja, and demanded that he be compelled to pay the price of the pan of meat-balls.

The Hodja listened attentively, then drew two coins from his pocket.

'Come here a minute,' he said to the restaurant owner.

The latter obeyed, and the Hodja enclosed the coins in his fist and rattled them in the man's ear.

'What is the meaning of this?' said the restaurant owner.

'I have just paid you your damages,' said the Hodja. 'The sound of money is fair payment for the smell of food.'

THE Hodja had decided to sell his half of the house he lived in, and summoned the agent.

'This is the wrong time to sell,' said the latter. 'What is the hurry?'

'I do not like sharing the house with anybody else,' replied the Hodja. 'I must sell my half to get the money to buy the other half.'

THE Hodja went hunting for wolves in the forest with a friend. Suddenly they spied a huge grey wolf, and set off after it as fast as they could. The wolf ran swiftly off, and disappeared into a hole in a grassy bank. The Hodja's friend tried to follow him into the hole, but got

44

stuck half-way in. The Hodja seized him by the feet and pulled him out. He had no head.

The Hodja was much perplexed, and making his way back to town, sought out his friend's wife.

'Tell me,' he said, 'did your husband have his head on when he left this morning?'

T HE Hodja managed to catch some quails. Plucking them and roasting them in the oven, he placed them in a large pot, put the lid on, and went off to summon his friends to the feast.

While he was gone, someone came and took his roast quails away, and put live ones in their place.

The Hodja arrived back with his friends, placed the pot in the middle of the table, and lifted off the lid.

Immediately the quails took flight and disappeared out of the window.

The Hodja was greatly dismayed.

'God,' he said, '*that* was a miracle indeed, and it is your right to bring the dead back to life. But what have you done with my firewood, my butter, my salt, my pepper, my spices, and all my labour?'

W HEN the Hodja was *cadi*, a peasant came to him and said:

'If your cow was grazing in the field with ours and killed one of ours, what is the law?'

'An animal cannot be called to account for the blood it spills,' replied the Hodja.

'I am very relieved,' said the peasant. 'Actually my cow killed yours.'

'That complicates the matter,' said the Hodja. 'Be so kind as to hand me down that little black book from the shelf.'

45

O<small>N</small> two or three occasions the Hodja brought home some lambs' liver. His wife gave it to a good friend of hers, and when the Hodja returned in the evening, all he got was a bowl of rice.

'Wife!' said the Hodja, at last. 'I cannot understand it. Lately I have been bringing some lambs' liver home, and yet I never seem to get a taste of it.'

'The cat steals it,' said his wife.

The Hodja picked up the chopper, and placed it in the trunk.

'From whom are you hiding the chopper?' asked his wife.

'From the cat, of course,' said the Hodja.

'The cat will not touch the chopper,' said his wife.

'If the cat will steal liver which costs only two *akches*,' replied the Hodja, 'it is capable of stealing a chopper which costs forty *akches*!'

T<small>HE</small> Hodja was once invited to dinner. His host ordered his servant to bring a number of dishes, including boiled figs with cream to finish on. All the other dishes arrived, but the boiled figs failed to appear.

'Before we retire to bed,' said the host to the Hodja, 'read us a passage from the Qoran to purify our spirit.'

The Hodja opened the Qoran at the passage which begins: 'By the figs and the olives and Mount Sinai'.

' "In the name of most merciful God",' recited the Hodja. ' "By the olives and Mount Sinai . . .".'

His host interrupted him.

'You have forgotten "the figs",' he said.

'I did not forget them,' said the Hodja, 'you did!'

T HE Hodja thought he would earn some money by dealing in salt vegetables. He set out through the town with his donkey laden on both sides with these provisions. The Hodja wanted to attract attention to his wares by calling them out, but every time he opened his mouth to shout 'Salt vegetables!', the donkey brayed, and no customers came.

They arrived in a busy part of the street.

'Salt vegetables!' called the Hodja, but the donkey brayed, and drowned his voice.

'Look here!' said the Hodja angrily to the animal. 'Am *I* selling these salt vegetables, or are *you*?'

Noting that a wedding was being celebrated in a near-by house, the Hodja folded a piece of paper, placed it in an envelope, and knocked on the door.

When the door opened, he told the servant that he had a message for the owner of the house, and was let in. Handing the envelope to the owner, he sat down at the richly laden table and began to eat.

His involuntary host opened the envelope and took out the paper.

'There is nothing written on it!' he said. 'It is quite blank!'

'I was in a great hurry,' said the Hodja, 'and your friend did not have time to write anything on it.'

Once when Timur Leng had his headquarters at Ak-Shehir he went on a tour of inspection of his troops, who were stationed about the countryside. On his return at the end of the week, the Hodja asked him if his trip had been enjoyable.

'Most enjoyable,' said Timur, who was noted for his cruelty. 'On Saturday there was a fire. On Sunday a mad dog bit a couple of people who had to have their wound cauterized with red-hot iron. On Monday a whirlwind blew down a number of houses and trapped the people inside. On Tuesday a bull broke loose and gored a large number of men. On Wednesday a man went mad and committed a murder, and had to be tortured. On Thursday a woman hanged herself on a plum-tree. On Friday I returned. It was a very pleasant week.'

The Hodja, who was trembling at the thought of all these calamities, lifted up his hands and began to praise Allah.

'What are you praising Allah for?' asked Timur.

'I am praising him for your return,' said the Hodja. 'Had you stayed any longer, your light, fantastic, tripping toe would have left not one stone upon another!'

48

T<small>HE</small> Hodja went into a mill and began to take handfuls of wheat out of the miller's sacks and put them in his own.

The miller came in.

'What are you doing there?' he demanded.

'I am a fool,' replied the Hodja. 'I have to do whatever comes into my head.'

'How is it, then, that it never comes into your head to take corn out of your sack and put it in mine?' asked the miller.

'I am an ordinary sort of fool,' said the Hodja, 'not a benighted imbecile!'

O<small>NE</small> day the Hodja was eating a roast chicken, when a man came up and asked him for a piece.

'I cannot give you any,' said the Hodja. 'It does not belong to me, but to my wife.'

'But you are eating it!' remarked the other.

'What am I to do?' pleaded the Hodja. 'My wife told me to.'

A boy came up to the Hodja, and pointing to another one near by, cried, and said that he had bitten him in the ear.

'That is not true!' said the second boy. 'He bit himself in the ear!'

'Shut up, you rascal!' said the Hodja. 'Is he a camel, that he can bite his own ear?'

O<small>NE</small> day the Hodja felt hungry.

'If only I had a bowl of hot soup,' he thought, 'I should be very happy!'

Just then there was a knock at the door. On the threshold stood a small boy with a bowl.

'My mother is not feeling well,' he said. 'Can you spare a little hot soup?'

'By Allah!' exclaimed the Hodja. 'Not even my thoughts are my own. I have only to *dream* of soup and my neighbours smell it!'

WHEN he was a young boy, the Hodja was so obstinate, and so disobedient, that his father, to get anything done at all, had to ask him to do the opposite of what he wanted him to do. If he wanted him to go to the right, he would tell him to go to the left.

One day, on their way back from the mill, they came to a narrow bridge, which the donkey, being laden with a large sack of flour, could not cross. The stream was, however, not deep.

'My son,' said the Hodja's father, 'I am going to cross this bridge. On no account lead the donkey across the stream.'

The Hodja grasped the donkey by the bridle and began to lead it across the stream. His father noticed, however, that the sack of flour was sagging down too much on the left side of the donkey, and would get wet if the donkey went any deeper into the water.

'My son,' cried the father anxiously, 'on no account put the sack level on the donkey's back. Pull it down a little towards the water.'

'Father,' said the Hodja, 'for years I have disobeyed you, and never done what you asked me. Now I am ashamed of myself. I shall do as you ask for once.'

And so, of course, the flour got very wet.

A merchant once stayed overnight in a caravanserai. The owner prepared him a meal of roast chicken in the evening, and two boiled eggs in the morning. When the time to depart came, the merchant vas in a great hurry, and promised to pay for his meals the next time he passed through. Three months later the merchant returned to the caravanserai and the owner again prepared him a roast chicken in the evening, and two boiled eggs in the morning. Before he departed he asked the owner what he owed him, reminding him not to forget the two meals from the previous occasion. In his mind he reckoned it ought to come to ten *akches* at the most.

'That will be two hundred *akches*,' said the owner.

'Two hundred *akches*!' exclaimed the astonished merchant. 'How is that possible?'

'Well,' replied the crafty owner, 'much of it is interest. Look at it this way. From me you borrowed for a period of three months one chicken and two eggs. In this space of time the chicken would have grown up and laid many eggs, and the eggs would themselves have become chickens, and then have laid eggs themselves, which would then in turn have become chickens, and laid more eggs, which would have become chickens, and so on. So you can see that such a large number of chickens and eggs can easily come to two hundred *akches*. I wonder, in fact, if I am not asking you for too little.'

The merchant angrily refused to pay the two hundred *akches*, and the owner of the caravanserai took him to court. The *cadi* was a friend of his, and ordered the merchant to pay the sum demanded. He was in great despair, and a friend advised him to consult Nasreddin Hodja to see if he could help. He announced his intention to call a witness, and the *cadi* granted a stay of execution for three days, stating a fixed time at which the hearing would take place.

The merchant went to see the Hodja, who agreed to help him as best he could.

When the hour for the hearing arrived, the *cadi* saw to his annoyance that the witness was not yet in court. He sent a messenger to fetch the Hodja, and finally the latter arrived in court two hours late.

'Why are you so late?' demanded the *cadi*.

52

'I am sorry, effendi,' replied the Hodja. 'I had boiled some corn to make into a pudding, when I decided that I should do better to plant it and reap a rich harvest in the autumn. I was planting it in my field when your messenger arrived. I am very sorry.'

'What fools there are in the world!' exclaimed the *cadi*. 'What will come from boiled corn?'

'About as much,' replied the Hodja, 'as will come from roast chickens and boiled eggs!'

The *cadi* reversed his decision and dismissed the case.

T HE Hodja was once travelling in a sailing-boat when a fierce squall arose, which tossed the ship from side to side and tore the topsail. When the Hodja saw the sailors rush aloft and start to tie up the sail, he was much perplexed.

'What are you doing?' he cried. 'If you want to keep the boat still, you should tie it at the bottom, not at the top!'

O NE day the Hodja and his friends began to talk about *helva*, a sweetmeat much appreciated in the Middle East.

'I like it very much,' said the Hodja, 'but I have never been able to make any.'

'Why not?' asked his friends.

'Whenever there was flour in the house, there was no butter; and whenever there was butter, there was no flour,' replied the Hodja.

'Do you mean to say,' exclaimed his friends, 'that it never in all these years happened that there was flour and butter in your house at the same time?'

'It sometimes happened,' replied the Hodja, 'but then I was not at home myself.'

ONE hot summer's day the Hodja dismounted from his donkey and lay down to rest in the shade of a walnut-tree at the edge of an egg-plant patch. He began to think.

'How strange of God it is,' he mused, 'that he should cause a large fruit like the egg-plant to grow on the end of a tiny stalk, and a small fruit like a walnut to grow on an enormous tree. Surely it would have been better if walnuts grew on little stalks, and egg-plants on trees.'

At that moment a walnut fell from the tree and hit the Hodja, small as it was, hard on the top of the head. The Hodja ruefully rubbed his skull.

'All is for the best in this world,' he thought. 'If egg-plants grew on trees, my head would have been smashed to pieces!'

ONE day a friend entrusted a jar to the Hodja and asked him to keep it for him until he came back. A few days passed, and the Hodja, who had been very curious to know what was in the jar, grew more and more impatient. Finally he took off the lid, and looked inside. The jar was full of honey. The Hodja dipped his finger in, and tasted the honey. It was excellent. The Hodja replaced the lid, and went about his business. It was not long, however, before his mind returned to the delicious honey. Off came the lid, in went the finger, on went the lid, and the Hodja went about his business. So it continued until the jar was wiped clean of any trace of honey. The owner returned and asked for the jar he had entrusted to the Hodja. It felt rather light, and he looked inside.

'Hodja!' he exclaimed. 'Where is my honey?'

'How nice it would be if you hadn't asked that question,' sighed the Hodja, 'and I didn't have to reply!'

THE Hodja loaded his donkey with two large basketfuls of grapes and set off for the market. On the way he met a group of children who danced for joy when they saw so many grapes.

'Effendi, effendi!' they cried. 'Give us some!'

'There are about twelve children here,' thought the Hodja. 'If I give everyone a grape, I shall lose money!'

So he broke off a stalk with three grapes on it, and gave it to one of the boys.

'Effendi!' cried the children. 'Is that all you can give us?'

'Look!' said the Hodja. 'All the grapes in these baskets taste the same. It therefore makes no difference whether you taste a quarter or a hundred!'

ONE windy day the Hodja was perched on top of a camel trying to eat a bowl of finely ground corn. Every time he raised his fingers to his mouth, a gust of wind blew the corn away before it reached his lips.

A friend passed.

'Hodja, what are you eating up there?' he called.

'If it goes on like this,' grumbled the Hodja, 'nothing!'

ONE winter the Hodja was having difficulty in making both ends meet, and in order to save what he could, he thought of giving his ass a little less barley. He accordingly subtracted a handful from the normal amount, gave the rest to the ass, and noted that it seemed to be quite content with what it had. A little while afterwards he subtracted another handful, and still the ass seemed happy. Soon the ass was receiving no more than half its normal ration. Admittedly, it grew rather quiet, but the Hodja thought it was still sound and healthy. He continued the process, and the ass grew more and more listless until, when its ration had fallen to one handful of barley, it refused to touch even this. One morning when the Hodja entered the barn he found his ass stone-dead.

'What bad luck!' said the Hodja. 'Just when I was succeeding in teaching my ass true mortification of the flesh, death had to intervene and spoil it!'

ONE day the Hodja planted some saplings in his garden. When evening came and he had finished his task, he uprooted them all, and carried them back into the house.

'Hodja, what are you doing?' asked their neighbour.

'We are living in bad times,' replied the Hodja. 'It is better to keep one's belongings where one can see them.'

THE Hodja's wife died, but he showed no signs of grief. Not long afterwards his donkey died, and there seemed no end to his weeping and lamentation and beating of breast.

'Hodja,' said a friend, 'when your wife died, you showed no emotion at all; but now, when your donkey dies, you weep and cry and shed a flood of tears. How is one to explain this?'

'My friend,' said the Hodja, 'when my wife died, many people came to me and told me not to worry, that they would find me an even better wife. Since my donkey died, however, no one has offered to find me a better donkey!'

ONE day the Hodja visited a village not far from Ak-Shehir. As he was walking through the village, a man came up to him and said:

'Effendi, what day is it today?'

'I am a stranger here,' replied the Hodja, 'you must ask one of the local inhabitants.'

A man once asked the Hodja:

'Do you know anyone in our town who can keep a secret?'

'I only know,' replied the Hodja, 'that one cannot expect other people to act as one's warehouse. It is therefore best to keep one's secrets to oneself.'

ONE day in winter, hearing people complain how cold it was, a man said to the Hodja:

'Some people are never content! In the winter they say, "How cold it is!", and in the summer, "How hot it is!"'

'Yes,' said the Hodja, 'but have you noticed one rarely complains in the spring?'

A friend of the Hodja was involved in a court-case concerning a number of sacks of wheat and he asked the Hodja to tell lies on his behalf.

When the Hodja was questioned, he began to talk in great detail about sacks of barley.

Finally, the *cadi* observed that he was supposed to be giving evidence concerning sacks of wheat, not barley.

'Effendi!' exclaimed the Hodja. 'If one is lying, does it matter whether one lies about wheat or barley?'

ONE day the Hodja went to the bazaar and saw a scimitar priced at three thousand *kurush*. The Hodja examined the sword, but could not see why it should cost so much money. He asked the people sitting in the coffee-shop near by if they knew the reason.

'That is a very fine scimitar,' they said. 'If you attack the enemy with that, it seems to stretch to five times its present length!'

The Hodja went home, found the fire-tongs, and took them to the bazaar.

'Who'll buy this fine pair of tongs?' he cried. 'Who'll give me three thousand *kurush* for these fine tongs?'

The people who were sitting in the coffee-shop called the Hodja over and began to examine his tongs.

'These are very ordinary things,' they said. 'What has possessed you to ask three thousand *kurush* for them?'

'When my wife is angry and comes at me with these tongs,' said the Hodja, 'they seem to stretch to ten times their present length!'

TIMUR Leng once asked the Hodja how long men would continue to be born and die.

'When heaven and hell are full up,' said the Hodja, 'it will stop.'

ONE day the Hodja gave his bag to a *hammāl* or porter to carry, and walked behind him through the bazaar. In the crowd, however, he lost sight of the man, and although he looked everywhere for him, he could not find him, or his bag.

A week later the Hodja was traversing the bazaar with a friend, when the latter said:

'Look, Hodja, there goes the porter you were looking for!'

The Hodja immediately dashed up a side-turning and hid.

His friend followed him.

'Hodja, what are you hiding for?' he asked. 'You have been looking for the *hammāl* all week, and now that you can get hold of him, you run away!'

'I am no fool!' said the Hodja. 'If he sees me, he will say that he has been carrying my bag around all week, and I shall have to pay him for seven days!'

ONE day the Hodja was talking with his friends and said:

'When I die, I want you to have me buried upside down.'

'Why?' they asked, in some bewilderment.

'When the end of the world comes and everyone is cast headlong down, I shall be the only one the right way up!' he said.

A peasant's goat contracted the mange, which in those days was cured by applying a coat of tar to the affected parts. The peasant, however, was a superstitious man, and he took his sick goat to the Hodja.

'Effendi,' he said, 'my goat has the mange. Breathe on it for me and it will be cured.'

For it was the custom, when a man fell ill, for a holy man to recite prayers over the victim, and then to breathe on him.

'Very well,' said the Hodja, 'I shall breathe on your goat for you. But if I were you, I shouldn't be sparing with the tar!'

ONE day the Hodja's wife felt unwell and asked her husband to fetch the doctor.

The Hodja, very worried, ran out of the house and up the street. As he passed the window, however, his wife stuck her head out.

'It's all right!' she called. 'God be praised, the pain has ceased. I do not need the doctor after all.'

The Hodja ran up to the doctor's house and knocked on the door.

'Doctor,' he panted, 'my wife fell ill, and asked me to fetch you. As I was leaving, however, she suddenly felt better, and sticking her head out of the window, told me she didn't need the doctor. I have therefore come to tell you you need not bother to come.'

THE Hodja took his donkey to market and handed it to the horse-dealer to sell for him.

'Gentlemen, come and look at this fine beast!' shouted the dealer. 'It is as strong as a lion, as gentle as a lamb, as swift as an eagle, as patient as the prophet Job.'

Carried away by the dealer's eloquence, the crowd began to bid for the donkey, and the price went up and up.

'By Allah,' thought the Hodja, 'that donkey is a good one, all right!' And he too began to bid. Eventually he outbid all the others, and thrusting the money in the astonished dealer's hand, he hastened home with his prize, and related his great triumph to his wife.

'I also got a bargain today,' she said. 'The cream-seller came to the door and I ordered a pot of cream. When he wasn't looking, I placed my bracelet on the side of the scale containing the weights, and so got much more cream than I should have got. I snatched the jug up and ran indoors before he should find my bracelet and realize how I had cheated him!'

'May Allah be praised for giving us such intelligence!' cried the Hodja. 'As a team we are quite unbeatable!'

T HE Hodja went to market and bought a sack full of vegetables. This he slung over his shoulder, and then mounted his donkey.

On the way he met some friends.

'Hodja,' they said, 'surely you are uncomfortable balancing that large sack on your shoulder with one hand and trying to guide your donkey with the other? Why not tie it to the donkey?'

'My donkey has enough weight to carry with me,' replied the Hodja. 'I shall carry the bag myself.'

T HE Hodja was once asked what was the more useful, the sun or the moon.

'The sun shines in the daytime when there is a lot of light already,' he replied, 'whereas the moon shines when it is dark. The moon is therefore much more useful.'

T HE village gossip, a notorious sponger, once said to the Hodja:

'I have just seen a gigantic stuffed turkey carried by on a huge plate.'

'What is that to me?' said the Hodja.

'They carried it to your house,' said the other.

'What is that to you?' said the Hodja.

T HE Hodja went to the *hammām*. The attendants gave him a tattered bath-robe and a worn-out towel, and paid no attention to him whatever.

The Hodja bathed and went out, leaving ten *akches* as a tip.

The attendants were astonished, but very pleased.

A week later the Hodja returned to the *hammām*. He was given a silken bath-robe, an embroidered towel, and the greatest attention.

The Hodja bathed and went out, leaving one *akche* as a tip.

'Effendi!' cried the attendants. 'What does this mean?'

'I see nothing strange,' said the Hodja. 'The tip I gave this time was for last time, and the tip I gave last time was for this time!'

A friend who could not write came to the Hodja and asked him to write a letter for him to an acquaintance in Baghdad.

'I have no time to go to Baghdad,' said the Hodja.

'I am only asking you to write a letter,' said the other. 'Why should you have to go to Baghdad?'

'My handwriting is so bad,' replied the Hodja, 'that no one can read my letters unless I am there to help them.'

ONE night the Hodja was lying in bed, when he heard a thief clambering over the roof of his house.

'Wife,' he said loudly, 'I forgot to tell you what happened when I got home this evening. I knocked on the door, but could not make you hear. So I prayed such-and-such a prayer, and taking hold of a moonbeam, slid gracefully down it into the bedroom.'

The thief, hearing this and noting the exact words of the prayer, repeated it, grasped a moonbeam in both hands, and stepped softly into space. Within a very short time he arrived, albeit not very grace-

64

fully, in the Hodja's bedroom. He felt he had hardly a bone in his body still intact.

The Hodja pounced on him, and grabbed him roughly by the scruff of the neck.

'I have caught him, wife!' he cried. 'Bring me some rope!'

'Don't worry,' groaned the thief, 'I'll not get away. You have a mighty powerful prayer, and I have a powerfully thick head!'

A neighbour once asked the Hodja:

'Is it true that you have vinegar forty years old?'

'Yes,' said the Hodja.

'Give me some, Hodja,' said the neighbour.

'I cannot, on principle,' said the Hodja.

'What principle?' asked the neighbour.

'On the principle that if I had given the vinegar to everyone who asked for it, I should not *have* any vinegar forty years old,' said the Hodja.

O NE day the Hodja, about to take his pupils to the mosque, mounted his donkey back to front.

'Why are you sitting like that, effendi?' they asked.

'If I do not, you will be behind me when we go to the mosque and I shall not see you. And if you go in front, I, your master, will be behind you.'

W HEN the Fast of Ramazān was over, the Hodja set out in search of the customary donations the Muslims give to their religious men who have devoted their lives to the pursuit of learning and wisdom. He arrived in a town a good distance from Ak-Shehir and spent the night in the house of a wealthy and respected citizen. In the morning the owner of the house summoned the Hodja, and asked him to read something out of the Qoran. The Hodja did so, and when he had finished, the learned layman read the selfsame passage as fluently as the Hodja. Then he asked the Hodja to write something. The Hodja did so, and his host wrote the same verses neatly and accurately.

'Well, Hodja,' he said, 'you see that I can read and write as well as you. You are going to ask me for a donation, but why should I give it? You are clearly not of any use to me. We are, in fact, equal.'

'You can read and write,' replied the Hodja, 'but we are not equal.'

'How is that?' said the other.

'When you have walked thirty miles and returned tired, empty-handed and humiliated, then you will be my equal!'

O NE day, very early in the morning, the Hodja learnt from voices under his window that the cart outside was just leaving for his home-town, Sivri-Hisar. He leapt out of bed without a stitch of clothing on him and climbed into the cart.

Since the Hodja was a most respected personality, no one said anything. As they neared Sivri-Hisar, the carter send word on ahead of the Hodja's imminent arrival.

All the peasants, delighted at this news, ran out to meet him. They were much taken aback when they saw their honoured compatriot as naked as his mother had borne him.

'What does this mean, Hodja?' they said.

The Hodja did not want to admit that he had been quick to take advantage of a free ride.

'I was so excited at the prospect of seeing you again', he said, 'that I forgot to dress.'

66

ONE day Timur Leng rather ridiculously invited the Hodja to a game of polo. The Hodja, of course, did not possess the agile pony necessary, and he arrived on the field seated upon an enormous ox.

All the spectators began to laugh.

'Hodja,' said Timur, 'for this game you need a pony as swift as a bird, and you arrive on an ambling ox. Why?'

'I have not played this game for fifteen years,' said the Hodja, a little red round the ears, 'but then my mount was a young calf, and no pony, nay, nor any falcon, could have overtaken him.'

ON another occasion Timur invited the Hodja to a hunt, and giving him a sorry nag, set off. Not long after, it began to pour with rain, and everyone turned about and galloped back. The Hodja's horse could not go very fast, and he saw that if he continued like that, he would be drenched to the skin. So he removed his clothes, and put them under the saddle. It stopped raining before he arrived back at the court, and he dismounted, dressed, remounted and rode back. Timur noticed that the Hodja had not got wet at all.

'How is it, Hodja,' he said, 'that you are the only one of us who did not get wet?'

'It is due to that fine horse you gave me,' replied the Hodja. 'One touch of the spur, and he flew like the wind, and not a single drop of rain fell on him!'

Timur had the Hodja's mount quartered in his best stable.

After a few days, another hunt was arranged, and the Hodja was again invited. This time Timur took the Hodja's horse. Again it came on to rain, and Hodja and the others galloped swiftly back to the court, leaving Timur to amble back in the pouring rain. He got very, very wet, and very, very angry.

'Why did you lie to me, Hodja?' he said. 'Thanks to you and this wretched horse I have got drenched to the skin!'

'That is your own fault, Your Majesty,' said Nasreddin. 'You didn't handle it right! If you had only put your clothes under the saddle like me, you wouldn't have got them wet!'

ONE day when walking past the cemetery, the Hodja saw a dog, an animal the Muslims hold to be especially unclean, rummaging around a grave. The Hodja lifted his stick to strike at the dog, but it suddenly bared its teeth, and moved towards the Hodja with a menacing snarl.

The Hodja backed hurriedly, and smiled a forced smile.

'Don't let me disturb you,' he said. 'Carry on, boy!'

ONE day the Hodja prepared to set off with the caravan. A horse was brought for him, and putting his right foot in the left stirrup, the Hodja vaulted up, and found himself back to front, with the horse's head behind him.

'Ho, there!' cried the Hodja, angrily. 'You have given me a left-handed horse!'

One day the Hodja's wife, just to spite him, prepared a very pep-pery soup and served it boiling hot.

Not thinking of what she was doing, however, she scooped up a large spoonful of the soup and swallowed it. The burning pain in her mouth caused tears to come to her eyes, but she said nothing lest it should discourage the Hodja from tasting his.

But he noticed the tears in her eyes.

'What are you crying for, wife?' he said.

'I was thinking how my poor, dear mother liked this soup,' she said, 'and now she is dead and gone!'

The Hodja murmured a word of sympathy, and swallowed a large spoonful of soup.

Tears came into his eyes also.

'What's the matter with you?' said his wife, with a note of triumph. 'What are you crying for?'

'I am crying because your poor, dear mother is dead and gone,' replied the Hodja, 'whereas you, you good-for-nothing, are still alive!'

One day the Hodja said, when the question of inventing new dishes was raised:

'I once invented the idea of eating bread and snow, but even I did not like it.'

THE Hodja was sitting up a tree in somebody else's garden eating the apricots when the owner passed by. Nasreddin made a valiant attempt to conceal himself in the foliage.

'What are you doing up that tree?' asked the owner, sternly.

'I am a nightingale and I have come here to sing,' replied the Hodja.

'All right, sing, then!' said the owner.

The Hodja began to whistle, feebly, wetly, and very much off-key.

The owner of the garden grinned in spite of himself.

'Is that how a nightingale should sing?' he said.

'I am only a young nightingale,' said the Hodja. 'I am still learning!'

ONE day an acquaintance complained to the Hodja that his eyes ached, and asked his advice.

'The other day one of my teeth started to ache,' said the Hodja, 'and I had no peace until I had it out.'

ONE day the Hodja was asked:

'How is it that as soon as day breaks and people get up, some go off in one direction, and some in others?'

'If everybody went off in one direction,' said the Hodja, 'the earth would tip over.'

ONE day when the Hodja was walking outside the town, a large bird flew out of a thicket, and gave the Hodja such a fright that he was sure he had passed away. He lay on the ground for a long time, but nobody came by to see him and take his body home. Besides, he was growing very hungry. Finally, in the late afternoon, he got up, walked home, told his wife how, when and where he had died, and returned to his place in the woods.

His wife began to beat her breast, tear her hair and lament loudly, and running to her neighbours, she told them of the death of her poor husband. They asked her where he had died.

'In the woods outside the town,' she said.

'Who told you?' they said.

'That is the most terrible thing!' she said. 'He died all alone, with not a friend to help him. And despite the state he was in, the poor man had to walk all the way back home to tell me himself!'

ONE day the Hodja dropped his ring inside the house. Not finding it there, he went outside and began to look round the doorway. His neighbour asked him what he was looking for.

'I have lost my ring,' said the Hodja.

'Where did you lose it?' asked the neighbour.

'In my bedroom,' said the Hodja.

'Why, then, are you looking for it out here?'

'There's more light out here,' he said.

ONE day when the Hodja was acting as *cadi*, a man came up and claimed that his lute, which had been stolen, had turned up for sale in the bazaar, and he asked the Hodja to have it returned to him. The Hodja summoned the merchant, and asked him to show cause why he should not return the lute to the man who claimed to be the owner.

'It belongs to me,' said the merchant. 'I bought it in So-and-so.'

The Hodja then asked the two parties to prove their case. The merchant could produce nothing, but the plaintiff produced half a dozen witnesses. The Hodja questioned these.

'What have you got to say?' he said.

'The lute belongs to this man,' they said. 'The back is cracked, and one of the pegs is broken. We know it is his.'

On examination, the lute in the merchant's possession proved to correspond to this description, and the Hodja announced that it

71

should be returned to the plaintiff.

The merchant grew very angry.

'They have all seen this lute in my shop,' he said. 'Why do you believe them? That one is a known liar. That one a thief. None of them is any good morally!'

'They may be no good morally,' replied the Hodja, 'but when it comes to a quarrel about a lute, they are first-class witnesses.'

Three of his friends found the Hodja in the coffee-house.

'Come quickly!' they said. 'Your wife has lost her reason.'

The Hodja made no move.

'My wife, as long as I have known her, has never shown any signs of having any reason,' he said. 'How can she lose what she never had?'

The Hodja was riding home on his donkey, when he dismounted and went into the forest. Not wishing to risk tearing his *djübbeh*, he laid it on the donkey's saddle. While he was away, however, a thief came quietly up, stole the cloak, and moved silently off.

When the Hodja returned and saw that his cloak had gone, he undid the donkey's saddle and tied it on his back.

Then he hit the donkey with his whip.

'Give me back my *djübbeh*, you rogue,' he said, 'and I shall give you back your saddle!'

ONE evening the Hodja was drawing water when he saw the reflection of the moon at the bottom of the well.

'The moon has fallen down my well,' said the Hodja. 'If I do not get it out, it will be the end of the world, and everyone will blame me!'

He tied a large iron hook to the end of a piece of rope, and let it down the well. When he judged that he could hook the moon, he began to pull on the rope. The hook, however, had caught under a stone on the bottom of the well. The Hodja strained and pulled, until the hook suddenly dislodged the stone and flew up the well-shaft. The Hodja fell flat on his back.

'Allah be praised!' he said, seeing the moon in the sky. 'It was a great effort, but I have got it back where it belongs!'

THE Hodja's mule died, and he went to the bazaar to buy another. He chose a sound-looking beast, and set off home with it.

The two men he had bought it from, however, were a pair of thieves. They trailed the Hodja for some distance, then, when there was no one else around, they cut the rope by which the Hodja was leading the mule. One of the thieves took the mule back to the bazaar, while the other, fastening the rope round his neck, meekly followed the Hodja.

When the Hodja arrived at the door of his stable, he turned round and saw that he had a man on the end of his rope.

'What are you doing here?' he said.

'As a punishment for angering my mother, she turned me into a mule. But now I see that the fact of being bought by a good man has broken the spell, and I am a human being again,' explained the thief.

'Allah be praised!' exclaimed the Hodja. 'Go back to your mother. But take my advice! Do not anger her again.'

The next day he again went to the bazaar to buy a mule. There he saw the other thief with the self-same mule that he had bought the day before.

'You fool!' said the Hodja to the mule. 'Didn't I warn you not to anger your mother again?'

ONE day a gang of young village boys were playing under a large tree when they saw the Hodja approaching.

'We'll get him to climb this tree,' they said, 'and when he is up there, we'll steal his slippers.'

When the Hodja drew level, they danced about, shouting:

'Nobody can climb this tree! Nobody can climb this tree!'

'I'll climb it,' said the Hodja.

Tucking his skirts into his belt, he removed his slippers and placed them in the folds of his *djübbeh*.

'Hodja,' cried the boys, 'why are you taking your slippers with you?'

'Ah, my boys,' said the Hodja, 'who knows but all that foliage may conceal a road?'

ONE day the Hodja was sitting at his window upstairs, when someone knocked at the door.

'What do you want?' he asked, leaning out.

'Come down and I'll tell you,' said his visitor.

The Hodja went downstairs and opened the door. His caller was a
beggar.

'Give me alms,' he said.

'Come upstairs,' said the Hodja.

The beggar followed him upstairs. When they arrived at the window where he had been sitting, the Hodja said:

'No. God will help you.'

'Why did you not say "No" downstairs, instead of dragging me all
the way upstairs to tell me?'

'For the same reason that you dragged me all the way downstairs,'
said the Hodja.

THE Hodja was one day walking along the top of a ravine when he
met a burly and wild-looking shepherd.

'Hodja,' he said, 'you are a scholar, are you not?'

'Yes,' said the Hodja.

'Do you see all those bones and bodies at the bottom of the ravine?'
said the shepherd.

The Hodja looked down and was not comforted by what he saw.

'They belong to the people who could not answer the question I
posed them, and whom I therefore had to kill,' said the shepherd.
'I am going to ask you it now.'

'Ask,' said the Hodja.

'Well now,' said the shepherd, 'when the new moon comes it is a
mere sliver of silver. Then it grows into a disc the size of a wheel. Then
after the fifteenth day it grows smaller and smaller, and finally dis-
appears. Then another one appears. What I want to know is, what
happens to the old one?'

'Do you not know?' said the Hodja. 'They take it away and make it

75

into a mill-stone. Haven't you seen how the sparks fly during a thunderstorm?'

'Bravo, Hodja!' exclaimed the shepherd. 'That's what *I* always thought!'

ONE day a peasant brought the Hodja a hare, and went away. A week later he came again, but the Hodja did not recognize him.

'I am the man who gave you the hare,' said the peasant.

'Come in,' said the Hodja. The hare had long since been digested, but he placed a bowl of soup in front of his guest, and said:

'Have some hare-soup.'

A few days later a group of peasants approached the Hodja's house.

'We are the friends of the peasant who gave you a hare,' they said.

'Come in,' said the Hodja.

And he gave them also a bowl of soup.

Another week passed, and an even larger band of peasants arrived at the Hodja's door.

'Who are you?' asked the Hodja, although he already had a faint idea.

'We are the neighbours of the friends of the peasant who gave you a hare.'

'Come in,' said the Hodja.

And he set before each of them a bowl of water.

'Effendi!' they said, when they tasted it. 'What is this?'

'That is the water of the gravy of the hare of the friend of your neighbours,' he said.

ONE day the Hodja was walking across a field when an ox appeared and snorted at him. The Hodja gathered up his skirts, and running for dear life towards the hedge, dived to safety, but not without acquiring a few scratches.

A week passed.

Then, along the village street passed the offending ox, harnessed securely to a cart.

The Hodja raised his stick and began to beat the helpless ox.

'Hey!' cried the peasant with the cart. 'What are you doing to my ox? Leave him alone!'

'You keep out of this!' panted the Hodja. 'He knows why I'm beating him!'

ONE day the Hodja said to his friends:

'When I die, I want to be buried in an old grave.'

'Why?' they asked.

'When the angels who come to question a man on his sins come to me, I shall say: "I have already been questioned. Look, my grave is an old one!" That way I shall save myself a lot of trouble,' he said.

ONE day a friend came up to the Hodja with an egg hidden in his hand.

'Hodja,' he said, 'if you guess what I've got in my hand, I'll treat you to an omelette. An *omelette*.'

'Give me a clue,' said the Hodja.

'It's white on the outside, and yellow in the middle.'

'I know, I know!' cried the Hodja. 'It's a turnip with a carrot inside!'

ONE year, when the month of Ramazān came round and all Muslims were expected, according to the precepts of the Prophet Muhammad, to fast for the whole month, the Hodja suddenly got the useful idea that to vie with others denoted a lack of humility, and he decided not to fast after all, except perhaps on the last day. He decided to keep count of the days by putting stones, one for each day, into a bag. That way he would be sure to know when the thirtieth of the month arrived. Seeing that her father kept putting stones into a bag, his little daughter, to be of help, also began to put stones in it, unbeknown to the Hodja.

Towards the middle of the month the Hodja was asked what day it was.

'Wait a minute, and I shall tell you,' he said, and tipping the contents of his bag on to the ground, began to count. There were one hundred and twenty stones!

'If I tell him the truth,' thought Nasreddin, 'he'll never believe it. The common mind is baffled by the unusual. He'll probably even believe I am not all there!'

So turning to his companion, he said:

'It's the 45th.'

'How can that be, Hodja?' said the other. 'There are only thirty days *in* a month!'

'I was sparing you the truth,' said the Hodja. 'If you counted the stones, you would see it is really the 120th!'

78

ONE day the Hodja tried to mount a horse, but it was a fairly tall one, and he could not quite manage it, and slipped off.

'That's old age for you!' he muttered for the benefit of bystanders. But looking round, he saw that there was nobody there.

'Well,' he added, 'I was not all that good when I was young either!'

A neighbour asked the Hodja if he could borrow a clothes-line.

The Hodja disappeared indoors, and then returned.

'The line is in use,' he said. 'My wife has hung some flour on it.'

'Whoever heard of anyone hanging flour on a clothes-line!' exclaimed the neighbour.

'Only those people to whom one does not wish to lend it,' said the Hodja.

ONE day the Hodja took a ladder, propped it against the wall of an orchard, climbed over, and pulled the ladder after him. Unfortunately for him, the gardener had seen everything.

'What are you doing here?' he demanded.

'I am selling ladders,' said the Hodja.

'Does this look like the place to sell ladders?' asked the gardener.

'What a question!' exclaimed the Hodja. 'Do you think there is only one place to sell ladders in?'

WHEN the Hodja was still very young, a grown-up asked him: 'Who is older, you or your brother?'

The Hodja thought.

'Last year my mother told me that my brother was one year older than I. So this year we must be the same age,' he said.

One day the Hodja went to the town baths. As luck would have it, the baths were empty apart from him, and the Hodja opened his mouth and began to sing. He was very much pleased with his rich and resonant voice, and on leaving the baths, mounted the minaret, and began to sing out the noon-day prayer.

His voice caused a small sensation in the square below, but not the sort he expected.

'What are you doing up there, Hodja?' cried a voice from the crowd. 'Let the muezzin give the call to prayer. You've got a voice like a goat!'

The Hodja leant over the railing.

'Build a bath up here,' he shouted defiantly, 'then you'll see what a voice I have!'

One morning the Hodja entered a vegetable garden, and began to fill his sack with everything he could lay his hands on —carrots, marrows, aubergines, beans, and melons. Suddenly the owner appeared.

'What are you doing in there?' he said.

'Yesterday evening,' replied the Hodja, 'a terrible whirlwind swept me away and deposited me in this garden.'

'And who picked all these vegetables?' said the owner, pointing to the abundant contents of the sack.

'Ah. The whirlwind threw me with great force from side to side, and in order to remain on the ground, I seized hold of whatever I could, and it came away in my hand.'

'All right,' said the owner, grimly. 'And who put them in that sack?'

'Not so fast,' said the Hodja. 'I am still working on that one!'

ONE day the Hodja was walking outside the town, past the cemetery, when he saw a band of horsemen approaching. Fearing the worst and taking them for robbers, he threw off his *djübbeh* and shirt, and naked to the waist, jumped down into an empty, freshly dug grave.

When the horsemen drew level, they noticed the Hodja.

'What are you doing in that grave?' they asked.

Ever afterwards the Hodja was to be proud of his great presence of mind.

'I am dead really,' he said, 'but I thought I would take another look at the world!'

THE great lord of the Mongols, the terrible Timur Leng or Timur the Lame, spent some time in Ak-Shehir after his defeat of the Ottoman Turks at Ankara, and was on friendly terms with the Hodja.

On one occasion the Hodja was taking a dish of beetroots as a gift to offer the great conqueror, when he met a man who said he thought beetroots were not a suitable gift, and that Timur would prefer figs. So the Hodja changed the beetroots for a couple of *okkas* of figs, and took them to the court. Timur, who was used to expensive gifts of gold, silver, and precious stones was not pleased with this humble gift, and he ordered his men to pelt the Hodja with his figs.

As the figs rained on his head and shoulders, the Hodja began to offer loud thanks to the Most High.

'Allah be prais d!' he cried. 'Honour and glory to the All-merciful!'

Timur ordered his men to stop.

'Hodja,' he said, 'you have been grossly humiliated. What do you find to thank God for now?'

'I thank God I did not bring the beetroots!' said the Hodja.

On another occasion the Hodja came to see Timur. The conqueror's lame leg was hurting him, and he had it outstretched in front of him. Nor did he rise when the Hodja came in, as etiquette demanded. He bade the Hodja sit on the carpet near him. The Hodja was inwardly very angry, for he had not realized that Timur was in some pain, and thought that he was deliberately slighting him. When he sat down, therefore, he stuck out one foot in front of him, aping his host.

The Mongol flushed.

'It is clear that you are not far removed from a donkey, Hodja,' he said.

'No', said the Hodja. 'only a couple of yards,'

A Persian came to Ak-Shehir and began to tell the Hodja of the marvellous palaces built in Isfahan by the Shah, some of which had two hundred rooms and covered an area of thousands of square feet.

'That is nothing,'said the Hodja. 'In our capital in Bursa the Sultan has just built a hospital ten thousand feet long and . . .'

Just at that moment another Persian came in who had just returned from Bursa.

'. . . and one hundred feet wide,' concluded the Hodja.

'That is a most peculiar building,' said the first Persian. 'Why is its width not in proportion with its length?'

'It would have been,' replied the Hodja, 'if our friend hadn't suddenly arrived back!'

A man once complained to the Hodja that there was no sunlight in his house.

'Is there any sunlight in your garden?' said the Hodja.

'Yes,' replied the other.

'Then put your house in your garden,' said the Hodja.

ONE of the Hodja's friends had just had a house built, and he proudly invited the Hodja in to look it over. For hours on end he bored the Hodja with details of the construction, the cost, the site, and all the amenities of his new dwelling, but he quite omitted to offer him anything to eat. The Hodja grew faint with hunger. When his friend took him a second time into the dining-room, the Hodja began to pace out the length and breadth of the room, to estimate its height, to examine the fine woodwork of the walls, and anything else that caught his eye. All these details he noted down in a little note-book.

'I can see you like my dining-room,' said his friend. 'Are you going to rebuild yours like it?'

'I shall think about it, certainly,' said the Hodja. 'For what ruins a man nowadays? The price of food! And in the whole of your house, even in the dining-room, there is not the slightest sign of any of that!'

THE Hodja was sitting on the bank of a river, when ten blind men came up, and offered him ten *kurush* to take them across in a boat.

The Hodja began to propel them across, but not being a very skilled boatman, he caused the boat to lurch in midstream, and one of the blind men fell out and was carried away by the current. His companions began to holloa and shout.

'Oh, don't make such a fuss!' cried the Hodja. 'Pay me nine *kurush* and we'll call it quits!'

TIMUR Leng took the Hodja into the field where his archers were practising.

'I am very good at archery,' boasted the Hodja, and suddenly found himself faced with the task of proving it, for Timur commanded him to take his bow and loose some arrows at the target.

The Hodja took the bow and shot an arrow.

It flew past the target several feet wide.

'That is how the *cadi* shoots,' he said.

His second shot also went wide.

'That is how the mayor shoots,' he said.

His third shot, by a fluke, scored a bull's-eye.

'And that is how Nasreddin Hodja shoots!' he said proudly.

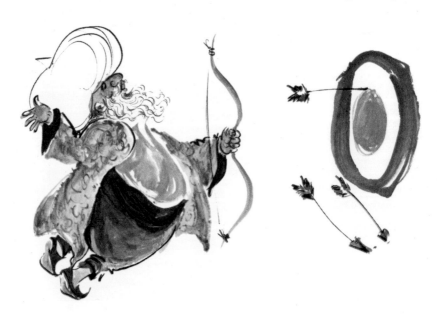

GRAPES were being sold very cheaply in the bazaar, but one of the Hodja's friends asked him to try to buy some for him still more cheaply.

The Hodja went to the bazaar and began to haggle with the merchant. In the end he managed to buy the grapes for a very low price.

When he returned, his friend asked him how he had fared.

'I succeeded,' said the Hodja. 'I haggled, and wheedled, and flattered, and pleaded, and told the merchant all manner of rubbish about economics and fair prices. Finally he believed my lies, and let me have the grapes a lot cheaper.'

'That is very good news,' said his friend. 'Bravo!'

'I did it on your encouragement,' said the Hodja, 'but will you agree that I have the right to consider my own interests?'

'Of course,' said his friend.

'Then since I did all the work, I shall keep the grapes for myself,' said the Hodja.

THE Hodja had given his daughter's hand to a man who lived in a neighbouring village. The marriage procession was already under way to the groom's house, when the Hodja realized that this was probably his last chance to give his daughter the advice she needed for the new married life upon which she was about to embark.

The Hodja accordingly set off at great speed in pursuit of the procession, and catching it up, he elbowed out of the way the women surrounding his daughter.

'Daughter,' he said, puffing and blowing, 'I have some important advice to give you. When you thread a needle, tie a little knot in the other end of the cotton, or it may pass straight through the eye of the needle.'

THE Hodja sent his daughter to fetch some water, and before she left, gave her a good box on the ears, saying:

'Mind you do not break the jugs!'

The girl burst into tears, and a crowd gathered.

'The girl has done nothing, Hodja,' they said. 'Why did you box her ears?'

'I did it to teach her the seriousness of breaking the water-jugs,' said the Hodja. 'One must do that before she breaks them. Afterwards it is too late!'

T HE Hodja was seated with his friends in the coffee-house when a man came up and asked him to change a gold piece for him. The Hodja had not got change for it, but he did not wish to admit it in front of his friends. He took the gold piece and weighed it thoughtfully in the palm of his hand.

'This coin is underweight,' he announced. 'I cannot change it for you at its face value.'

'That is all right,' said the other. 'Give me what you think it is worth.'

'It is very, very much underweight,' insisted the Hodja.

'I shall go and see the man I got it from later,' said the owner of the coin. 'Give me however much or little you think it is worth. You would do me a great service, as I need change.'

The Hodja, seeing that he would lose face if he did not think of something quickly, grew angry.

'This coin is so much underweight,' he said, 'that if I change it, you will owe *me* a shilling!'

A T one time the Hodja acted as the village schoolmaster. One of the parents, being very pleased with his son's progress, sent the Hodja a box of *baklava*, or honey-cakes. The Hodja had no time to eat them when they arrived, however, as he was obliged to attend to some business in the mosque.

He therefore shut the box of cakes in the drawer of his desk.

'Mind you do not touch these cakes, children,' he said. 'I am sure they have been poisoned by my enemies!'

And off he went.

Among the schoolchildren in the class, however, was the Hodja's nephew, who knew his uncle rather well. As soon as the Hodja was out of the school, he went to the drawer, took out the box, and offered to share the cakes with his class-mates.

'We daren't,' they said. 'They may be poisoned.'

'Of course they are not,' said the nephew, and put one into his mouth. 'They are very good.'

'But what will the Hodja do if he finds the cakes gone?' said the others.

'Leave that to me,' said the nephew.

And so the cakes were all gobbled up.

When the Hodja returned, he opened the drawer and took out the box. Not a crumb remained.

'Where are my cakes?' he thundered.

'I ate them,' said his nephew.

'*You* ate them!' spluttered the Hodja. 'How? Why?'

'I went to your drawer to get the penknife to sharpen my quill, and the knife broke. I knew how angry you would be, and decided to put an end to my life. I did not wish to defile the well, so I decided to eat the poisoned cakes that were in the drawer. But it's a funny thing, nothing happened!'

'It is funny indeed,' said the Hodja, 'and probably to do with something that runs in the family!'

ONE day a nasty fellow who thought himself very clever broke the Hodja's walking-stick to tease him. The Hodja had used the stick for many years, and was very upset.

'That stick was like my right hand,' he said. 'God will avenge me. When forty days have passed, you will break your leg!'

This curse wiped the grin off the other man's face, and he left the Hodja's house with a very worried expression. He was so preoccupied that he did not look where he was going, tripped over a stone and fell and broke his leg.

He hobbled back to the Hodja.

'This is not fair,' he said. 'You said I should break my leg after forty days, and I've broken it now.'

'That must be the result of someone else's curse,' said the Hodja, mercilessly. 'When my curse takes effect, you will have to crawl around on your hands and knees!'

THE Hodja was taking his donkey to sell in the market when he saw that its tail was dirty and very tangled. He cut it off and put it in his bag.

In the bazaar a prospective customer came up, but when he examined the donkey closely, he discovered what was missing.

'Ha, what is the good of a donkey without a tail?' he said.

'Let us first decide on a price for the donkey,' said the Hodja. 'The tail is not a thousand miles away!'

ONE day the Hodja passed through a village and was amazed to find that the inhabitants were all eating and drinking and making merry.

'What a prosperous village!' he exclaimed, when he too was presented with a large plate of sweetmeats. 'The people where I live are close to starvation!'

'But it is the same here,' said his hosts. 'Today is a feast day. Everyone in the village has saved something for today. That is why the village appears to be prosperous.'

The Hodja thought for a bit, and then sighed.

'If only every day were a feast day,' he said, 'no one would ever go hungry.'

THE Hodja was invited to an important banquet, and he went in his everyday clothes. No one paid any attention to him whatsoever, and he remained hungry and thirsty, and very bored. Eventually he slipped out of the house unobserved and made his way home. Here he changed into his best clothes, putting on a magnificent turban, a fine silk *binish*, and a large fur coat over all. Then he made his way back to the banquet.

This time he was welcomed with open arms. The host bade him sit beside him, and offered him a plate covered with the choicest delicacies.

90

The Hodja took off his fur coat and held it to the plate.

'Eat, my beauty!' he said.

'Effendi, what are you doing?' exclaimed his astonished host.

'It was the fur coat, not the man inside, which conjured up these delicacies,' replied the Hodja. 'Let it then eat them!'

THE Hodja went to the bazaar and chose a pair of trousers. The merchant had already made a parcel of them when the Hodja changed his mind, and decided that he was more in need of a light cloak.

'Give me a cloak instead,' he told the merchant, and when the parcel was ready, he picked it up and walked off.

'Effendi,' called out the merchant, 'you have not paid me for the cloak!'

'But I left you the trousers for it,' replied the Hodja.

'But you did not pay for the trousers,' said the merchant.

'I should think not!' said the Hodja. 'Why should I pay for trousers I did not take?'

FOR some reason that is now forgotten, the people of Ak-Shehir grew very angry with the Hodja, and complained of him to the *cadi*. The *cadi* summoned the Hodja, and said:

'The people here do not like you. Move somewhere else.'

'It is I who do not like the people here,' said the Hodja. 'Let them go, to the devil for all I care.'

'But they are many, and you are one,' said the *cadi*.

'Since they are many, they will be able to build a village wherever they go,' said the Hodja, 'but how can I, at my age, build a new house and cultivate a field in the mountains all alone?'

Someone asked the Hodja when he thought the end of the world would come.

'Which end of the world?' asked the Hodja.

'Why, how many ends are there?' exclaimed his interlocutor.

'Two,' replied the Hodja. 'When my wife dies, that will be the first. When I die, that will be the second.'

On another occasion he was questioned about the will of God.

'Is the will of Allah always done?' they asked him.

'For as long as I remember it has been,' replied the Hodja. 'If it were not so, surely my will would have stood a chance of being done once in a while.'

The Hodja took his donkey to market and entrusted it to a dealer to display it for him.

A prospective customer approached, and wishing to see how old the donkey was, opened its mouth to look at its teeth. The donkey promptly bit him hard on the hand. The customer jumped back, and went off nursing his hand and cursing.

A little later another customer arrived, and wishing to see whether the donkey was knock-kneed or not, walked round behind it. The donkey lashed out viciously with its hind hoofs, and caught the man a nasty blow on the shin. Hopping and cursing, the second customer went away.

This sort of thing went on for the rest of the day.

When the Hodja came back, the dealer said:

'Hodja, this donkey is crippling all my customers and ruining my reputation. Nobody wants to buy the vicious brute!'

'Oh, I do not want to sell it,' said the Hodja. 'I only wanted my fellow Muslims to see what I have to put up with from this beast!'

The Hodja left his house one morning and bumped into his neighbour.

'Hodja!' the neighbour exclaimed. 'I was very worried about you. I heard such a commotion in your house this morning, and there was a terrible bump. What happened?'

'My wife and I were having an argument,' said the Hodja, very reluctantly. 'She got very angry, and flung my *djübbeh* downstairs.'

'But Hodja,' insisted the bewildered neighbour, 'how can a *djübbeh* make all that noise?'

'If you must know,' said the Hodja, 'I was wearing it at the time.'

Seeing a number of ducks swimming in a lake, the Hodja made a quick dive towards them, but they all flew away.

The Hodja sat down at the side of the lake, took out the piece of dry bread which was his lunch, and dipped it in the lake.

A friend passed.

'Selām, Hodja,' he called. 'What are you eating?'

'Duck-soup,' replied the Hodja.

One night a thief entered the Hodja's house and began to stuff everything movable into a sack. Just then the Hodja came in. He began to help the burglar fill his sack. The man was speechless. Then he said:

'Effendi, what are you doing?'

'Oh, I thought we were moving,' said the Hodja.

For a joke his friends handed the Hodja a lute and asked him to play them a tune.

The Hodja took the quill in his right hand and strummed it back and forth across the strings. The sound was excruciating.

'Oh, is that how to play the lute, Hodja?' said his companions. 'We have observed that other players seek the note they want by moving the fingers of the left hand up and down the neck of the instrument.'

'I am not seeking any notes,' said the Hodja; 'I have found them!'

93

THE Hodja was walking home with a fine piece of liver when he met a friend.

'How are you going to cook that liver?' asked his friend.

'The usual way,' said the Hodja.

'That way it has no taste,' said the other. 'I have a very special way of preparing a very tasty meal with liver. Listen and I'll explain.'

'I am bound to forget it, if you tell me,' said the Hodja. 'Write it down on a piece of paper.'

The friend wrote out the instructions, and gave them to the Hodja, who continued his way home. Before he arrived at his door, however, a large crow swooped down, seized the liver in its claws, and flew high up into the sky with it.

'It won't do you any good, you rogue!' shouted the Hodja, triumphantly waving the piece of paper. 'I've got the recipe here!'

ONE day the Hodja put his chickens in a wicker basket, and set out for Sivri-Hisar. He had not gone far when he thought to himself:

'The poor birds will probably die of the heat, shut up in this basket. I'll let them out, and they can walk in front of me.'

No sooner had he let the chickens out of the basket, however, than they all began to run off in different directions.

The Hodja, red with anger, chased after the cock.

'You are a fine one!' he cried. 'You know when the sun is about to rise while it is still dark. But in the middle of the day, you don't even know the way to Sivri-Hisar!'

THE Hodja was extremely hungry, and when his wife laid a bowl of very hot soup in front of him, he seized his spoon and greedily swallowed a mouthful of soup before he realized how hot it was.

With a loud shout, he rushed out on to the street.

'Run for your lives, brothers!' he yelled. 'My belly's on fire!'

94

O<small>NE</small> day a man came up to the Hodja, and they began to gossip away together for a long time on all manner of private affairs. When the man rose to go, Nasreddin asked:

'Excuse me effendi, I do not recognize you. Who are you?'

'If you do not know me,' exclaimed the other, 'why have you been gossiping with me for the last hour without restraint, as if we were lifelong friends?'

'When you came up,' said the Hodja, 'I looked, and your turban was just the same as my own, and your *djübbeh* was just like mine. So I took you for me!'

O<small>NE</small> day the Hodja entered a village, and shortly afterwards found that he had mislaid his bag.

'You had better find my bag,' he said to the local peasants, 'or else . . .'

Since the Hodja was a well-known and honoured personality, the poor peasants could not know what influence he might have in high places, and they scoured the village from one end to the other until they finally found the missing bag. They handed it back to the Hodja.

One of the bolder peasants was bitten by curiosity.

'Effendi,' he said, 'what would you have done if we had not found your bag?'

'Oh,' said the Hodja, 'I have got an old piece of carpet at home, and would have made another one out of that.'

ONE evening a guest came to stay with the Hodja, and a bed was prepared for him in the Hodja's room. In the middle of the night, the guest said to the Hodja:

'Effendi, there is a candle on the right side of your bed. Please hand it to me so that I can light it.'

'Have you gone mad?' said the Hodja. 'How can I tell my right from my left in the dark?'

ONE night the Hodja awoke in great excitement.

'Wife! Get up! Light a candle!' he cried. 'I have been inspired. A magnificent poem! I must write it down before I forget it!'

His wife got up quickly, lit a candle, and brought her husband pen and paper. The Hodja seized the pen eagerly, wrote rapidly on the paper, and then fell back exhausted. He was about to snuff the candle, when his wife cried:

'Effendi, please read me your inspired poem.'

The Hodja, with a muffled protest, picked up the paper, and read:

> *'Among the leaves so green a black*
> *Hen with a red beak went "quack quack!"'*

ONCE when the Hodja was travelling through Anatolia he stayed overnight in a very old house in the country. Whenever the wind blew outside, the whole place creaked and swayed, and finally the Hodja called the *oda-bashi* or steward.

'I am sure those beams in the ceiling are loose,' he said, 'they creak all the time. Why do you not fetch a carpenter to see to them?'

'There is no danger,' said the *oda-bashi*. 'This place is a historic building of great antiquity, hundreds of years old. You are a *hodja*, and know that such a noble work proclaims the glory of God.'

'One can hear it,' said the Hodja. 'What I am afraid of is that it will be carried away by religious fervour, and come crashing down around our ears!'

W<small>HEN</small> his days were up and the Hodja, very old, lay on his death-bed, he said to his wife:

'Why are you dressed in black, with a tearful face and your hair all awry? Go and put on your gayest clothes, do your hair properly, and smile!'

'Hodja,' wept his wife, 'how can you ask me to do this? You are very ill, and I respect you.'

'That is why I ask you to do it,' replied the Hodja. 'The Angel of Death will be here any minute. If he sees you in all your finery, dressed like a peacock, he may leave me and take you instead!'

And with a chuckle, the Hodja died.

GLOSSARY

Aba	a heavy cloak.
Akche	a small whitish coin made of billon or silver.
Binish	a robe or cloak.
Cadi	a magistrate or judge.
Caravan	a band of merchants and others travelling together for safety and convenience, usually with laden camels.
Caravanserai	an inn where caravans put up for the night.
Djübbeh	a robe or cloak.
Effendi	a gentleman; 'Sir'.
Hammāl	a street porter.
Hammām	Turkish baths.
Helva	an oriental sweetmeat, made of various meals; a sort of candy.
Hodja	a learned man; a scholar.
Houri	a beautiful dark-eyed maiden awaiting the faithful in the Muslim Paradise, created from musk and spice.
Imām	a prayer-leader in a mosque.
Inshallah	'If God wills', an expression frequently used with statements referring to the future.

Kaftan	a robe or gown.
Kavuk	a scholar's turban.
Khātib	a preacher in a mosque.
Kurush	a small coin, a piastre (100 piastres = 1 *lira* or pound).
Mihrāb	a niche in a mosque indicating the direction of Mecca, towards which Muslims turn to pray.
Mimbar	a pulpit in a mosque.
Minaret	a tall tower attached to larger mosques from which the call to prayer is made five times a day, and twice at night.
Molla	a theologian; a doctor of divinity.
Mosque	a Muslim place of worship, in Turkish *djāmi* if large, and *mesdjid* (whence eventually the word mosque) if small and without a minaret.
Muhtar	an alderman, mayor.
Muezzin	he who performs the *ezan* or call to prayer.
Oda-bashi	a steward, porter, concierge.
Okka	a weight equivalent to roughly $2\frac{3}{4}$ pounds.
Qoran	the Muslim scriptures, the 'reading-book' *par excellence*, composed in Arabic.
Rebāb	a two-stringed bowed instrument, like a violin but held vertically.
Shish-kebāb	pieces of roast meat (*kebāb*) on a skewer (*shish*).
Sublime Porte	Turkish Court and Government.